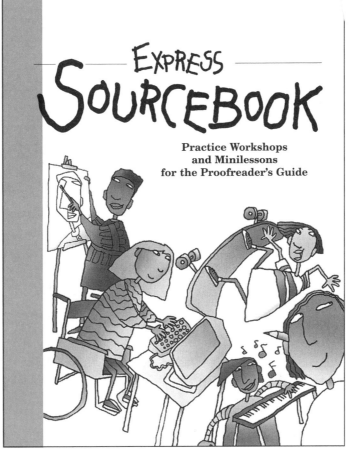

Express
SOURCEBOOK

**Practice Workshops
and Minilessons
for the Proofreader's Guide**

. . . a resource of student
workshops, minilessons, and
activities to accompany

WRITERS

EXPRESS

WRITE SOURCE

GREAT SOURCE EDUCATION GROUP
a Houghton Mifflin Company
Wilmington, Massachusetts

A Few Words About the Level 5 SourceBook

Before you begin . . .

You need to know that your SourceBook should be used with the *Writers Express* handbook, which provides information, examples, and models. The SourceBook provides you with opportunities to practice the editing and proofreading skills presented in the handbook. SourceBook activities are organized into Practice Workshops, Minilessons, and Check-It-Out Daily Sentences.

Practice Workshops

The Practice Workshops cover what you need to know to become a better writer and proofreader. The workshop topics appear in the same order in the SourceBook as they do in the Proofreader's Guide in the *Writers Express* handbook. In each workshop, The First Step introduces the basic idea and directs you to the handbook pages you will want to use. Each workshop has clear directions and examples. Follow-up writing activities are explained in The Next Step.

Minilessons

Each Minilesson covers one idea from the handbook. Most minilessons can be done on your own or with a partner.

Check-It-Out Daily Sentences

Check-It-Out Daily Sentences review basic writing skills. Focused Sentences help you concentrate on one editing skill at a time. Proofreading Sentences offer several different sentence problems for you to correct. Sometimes you will add a word, write a different word, or simply cross out a word. Such practice helps you become a more careful writer and a better proofreader.

Authors: Pat Sebranek and Dave Kemper

Printed in the United States of America

International Standard Book Number: 0-669-40263-X

4 5 6 7 8 9 10 - HLG - 01 00 99 98 97 96

Table of Contents

• Sentence Workshops

Understanding Sentences

Sentence Variety

Sentence Problems

Sentence Combining

• Language Workshops

Understanding Our Language

• Minilessons

Marking Punctuation

Editing for Mechanics

Checking Your Spelling and Usage

Understanding Sentences

Understanding Our Language

• Check-It-Out Sentences

Focused Sentences

• Check-It-Out Sentences

Proofreading Sentences

Practice Workshops

The practice workshops in this section of your SourceBook cover the basic language, editing, and proofreading skills you need to become a better writer.

End Punctuation 1

The First Step ● Choosing the correct **end punctuation** is a basic step in punctuating your writing. Your handbook explains when to use the three kinds of end punctuation: the period, the question mark, and the exclamation point. (See topic numbers 02, 54, and 56 in "Marking Punctuation," which starts on page 343.)

DIRECTIONS: Put the correct end punctuation—a period, a question mark, or an exclamation point—in the sentences below. You will also need to capitalize the first letter of each sentence. The first sentence has been marked for you.

H
ʜave you ever wondered who the very first Americans were꠸ scientists say they came from Asia thousands of years ago at that time, land connected Asia to the part of North America that is now Alaska imagine that

people followed herds of animals across the "land bridge" between Asia and America they needed these animals for food and clothing it was much too cold to grow crops the first Americans slowly moved farther and farther south after thousands of years, people reached the tip of South America

can you imagine living in a cave in a place where it is cold and snowy all the time no wonder people headed south

End Punctuation 1

The Next Step ● Write a paragraph describing your coldest experience. Try to use at least two words or phrases that might be followed by an exclamation point (Unbelievable!).

_____

_____

_____

_____

_____

_____

_____

_____

_____

_____

_____

_____

_____

End Punctuation 2

The First Step ● This activity gives you practice using correct **end punctuation**. Check your handbook (pages 343-351) if you need help with this activity.

DIRECTIONS: Put the correct end punctuation in the sentences below, and capitalize the first letter of each sentence. The first sentence has been marked for you.

The first superhero, Superman, came on the scene in 1938. he was created by a writer and an artist who lived in Ohio, and he was no average Joe how fast was Superman he was faster than a speeding bullet he was also strong enough to bend steel with his bare hands he had many special powers because he was from a planet called Krypton of course, he always used his powers to fight evil

Superman was so popular that he was in comic books and newspapers and on radio and TV when World War II started, Superman had millions of fans his creators had to decide whether Superman would join the army what did they decide well, Superman tried to join the army, but he failed his eye exam how could that have happened his X-ray vision caused him to read an eye chart in the next room, instead of the one he was supposed to read

End Punctuation 2

The Next Step ● Write a brief story describing a battle between Superman and a force of evil. Use the three kinds of end punctuation in your story. (*Hint:* You should be able to use lots of exclamation points.)

_____

_____

_____

_____

_____

_____

_____

_____

_____

_____

_____

_____

Using Commas 1

The First Step ● **Commas** are used between words or phrases in a series. Commas are used between two independent clauses that are joined by words such as *and, but, or, so,* and *yet.* (See handbook page 345, topic numbers 12 and 16.)

Examples:

Commas in a Series

People who do well in sprints are fast, strong, and dedicated.

Comma Between Two Independent Clauses

I used to run sprints, but now I am much more interested in the long jump.

DIRECTIONS: In the paragraph below, add commas between independent clauses and between items in a series. The first sentence has been marked for you.

Jessie Owens was a track star in the 1930's, and he was an African-American. He set six world records in 1935 and the next year he won four gold medals at the Olympics in Germany. Adolf Hitler, the German dictator, was a bigot so he didn't like the fact that Jesse Owens was the star of the Olympics. Owens also faced prejudice disappointment and unkindness in the United States. He had won four gold medals yet the award for best American athlete of the year was given to a white man who had won only one medal. However, a huge, noisy parade was held for Owens in New York City and someone threw a small, closed, white bag into his car. He thought there were cookies in the bag but he opened it and found $10,000 in cash!

Using Commas 2

The First Step ● **Commas** are used between words or phrases in a series and between two independent clauses that are joined by words such as *and*, *but*, or *so*. Commas are also used between items in dates. (See handbook page 345 and the examples below.)

Commas in a Series

The national anthem is as American as red**,** white**,** and blue.

Comma Between Two Independent Clauses

I know the words to "The Star-Spangled Banner**,**" but I can't hit all the notes! (**Note**: The comma is placed inside the quotation marks.)

Commas Between Items in Dates

I first heard the national anthem at a baseball game on July 4**,** 1988.

DIRECTIONS: In the paragraph below, add commas between independent clauses, between items in a series, and between items in dates. The first sentence has been marked for you.

Americans have been singing "The Star-Spangled Banner" since the early 1800's**,** but it wasn't our official national anthem until 1931. On November 3 1929 newspapers printed the news that there was no official anthem. Five million people wrote to ask Congress to choose one but many of them didn't want "The Star-Spangled Banner." Some people didn't like the fact that the music was written in England. After all, we had fought against England for our freedom. But the music to "Yankee Doodle " "Hail to the Chief " and other songs is also from England! "America the Beautiful " "America " and a few others received votes but "The Star-Spangled Banner" won the day.

Using Commas 3

The First Step ● Commas *again!* Well, commas are important! You'll be using them for the rest of your life, so it's important to use them right! Remember to check your handbook if you're not sure when or how to use commas. (See handbook page 345, topic numbers 12, 13, and 16.)

DIRECTIONS: In the paragraph below, add commas between independent clauses, between items in a series, and between items in dates. The first sentence has been marked for you.

Henry Ford invented the first mass-produced car , and he called it the Model T. The Model T was a big success but Henry Ford didn't stop there. On December 2 1927 a new model was introduced. Many people were curious about the new Model A so they flocked to see it. In Cleveland, police on horseback had to keep the huge, excited crowds in line. So that everyone could see it, the Model A was placed on a high platform in Kansas City. Ford salespeople said that the Model A rode smoothly gave a fast ride and was dependable. They also claimed that it had been clocked at 71 miles per hour! Every Model T was black but the new Model A came in new, exciting colors such as Arabian Sand and Niagara Blue.

Using Commas 3

The Next Step ● Write a basic news story announcing the development of a new car. Tell what makes the car special. Use commas correctly! (See pages 128-129 for help with your writing.)

Punctuating Appositives

The First Step ● As you know by now, commas are used in many different ways. This time, you're going to practice using commas to set off **appositives**. An appositive is a word or phrase that *renames* or *explains* the noun that comes before. (See your handbook, page 346, topic number 22.)

DIRECTIONS: Use commas to set off the appositives in the following sentences. The first two have been done for you.

1. Mrs. Chang‚ our teacher‚ won an award.

2. The award‚ a gift certificate‚ was for being an excellent teacher.

3. Our principal Mrs. Greene presented the award.

4. Mrs. Chang the best teacher I've had yet deserved to win.

5. Alisha who is in our class read a poem about Mrs. Chang.

6. Mrs. Chang's husband a math teacher was there.

7. The rest of us sang a song "You're the Best " for Mrs. Chang.

8. Bobby who wants to be a musician wrote the song.

9. Tamara a computer whiz made a banner on her computer.

10. The banner six feet long said, "Way to go, Mrs. Chang!"

Punctuating Appositives

The Next Step ● Write four sentences, each one saying something about a different person you know. Start each sentence with a person's name, then add an appositive that tells something about the person, and then finish the sentence. Use commas correctly!

1. _____

_____

_____

2. _____

_____

_____

3. _____

_____

_____

4. _____

_____

_____

Commas Between Clauses

The First Step ● Here's another place where **commas** signal readers to pause: after a long phrase or clause that introduces the rest of the sentence. Check out your handbook, page 346, topic number 23.

DIRECTIONS: In each of the following sentences, place a comma after the introductory phrase or clause. The first one has been done for you.

1. Invented by a British blacksmith in 1839, the bicycle became the world's most popular form of transportation.

2. Long before batteries or electricity a Greek inventor made a clock that was powered by moving water.

3. Better known as an astronomer Galileo invented the thermometer.

4. About 7,500 years ago in Turkey people used a natural glass called obsidian for mirrors.

5. A year before Thomas Edison introduced his light bulb a British inventor made one.

6. When the first movie was shown people fainted because they thought the train in the movie would run over them!

7. Although we don't think of it as such paper is an invention.

8. Invented in China in the year 105 paper is now used all over the world.

Commas and End Punctuation Review

The First Step ● This workshop activity is a review of commas and end punctuation. (See topic numbers 02, 54, 56, 12, and 16 in "Marking Punctuation," which begins on page 343 in your handbook.)

DIRECTIONS: Add needed commas and end punctuation marks in the sentences below. Also capitalize the first letter of each new sentence. The first sentence has been done for you.

In the early 1800's only about half of the kids in the United States went to school many people thought that only boys should go to school so girls were usually not allowed to attend a few special teachers thought that American schools should be open to girls, too

Sara Pierce started a school for girls and she taught grammar reading writing and history one of her students was Harriet Beecher Stowe ms. Stowe later wrote a famous novel called *Uncle Tom's Cabin*

the first college to accept women was Mount Holyoke College and it was started by Mary Lyon Emily Dickinson, another great writer, was a student there

one teacher became famous for writing books for both boys and girls he wrote the first American dictionary and his name is still on many dictionaries can you guess his name sure you can his name was Noah Webster

Using Semicolons

The First Step ● **Semicolons** can be confusing. What do they mean? What are you supposed to do with them? Well, first read about them on page 347 in your handbook. Then get some hands-on practice by doing these activities.

DIRECTIONS: Each sentence below contains two independent clauses that are separated by a conjunction and a comma. Cross out the conjunction and comma, and use a semicolon to separate the independent clauses instead. The first sentence has been marked for you.

Roy C. Sullivan was a park ranger; ~~but~~ his life was more exciting than you might think. He was struck by lightning seven times, but he lived to tell about it. No one understood why Sullivan kept getting hit by lightning, and it's amazing that he kept working! Lightning "fired" several of his hats, and one time it set fire to his hair.

The Next Step ● Semicolons are used to separate a series of phrases that contain commas. (See handbook page 347, topic number 26.) Write a sentence using the second set of phrases below.

buy cat food, cat toys, and litter ■ clean the cat box, hallway, and closet ■ give Fuzzball a good brushing

Example: *I'm supposed to buy cat food, cat toys, and litter; clean the cat box, hallway, and closet; and give Fuzzball a good brushing.*

see the lions, tigers, and bears ■ eat hot dogs, ice cream, and cotton candy ■ walk home in time for supper

© Great Source. All rights reserved.

Marking Punctuation **15**

Using Hyphens

> **The First Step** ● **Hyphens** are explained on page 348 in your handbook. The following two activities give you practice using them.

Using Hyphens to Join

DIRECTIONS: Put hyphens where they are needed in the sentences below. The first sentence has been marked for you.

1. Mom puts big pieces of chocolate in her chocolate ‿chunk cookies.

2. The governor elect has a lot to learn about her new job.

3. My great grandfather was a well known doctor.

4. I once made a long distance call to Japan.

5. My sister chews sugar free gum.

6. I have an eight year old cousin who looks like me.

Using Hyphens to Divide

DIRECTIONS: Use hyphens to divide the following words into syllables.

1. contents _____   6. history _____

2. writing _____   7. connection _____

3. item _____   8. arithmetic _____

4. revise _____   9. vocabulary _____

5. improving _____   10. apostrophe _____

> **The Next Step** ● Check your work by looking up each word in a dictionary. It will show you how to divide words into syllables.

Using Apostrophes 1

The First Step ● Apostrophes are sometimes used to show possession, other times to make contractions. There's a lot to learn about apostrophes. Start by reading page 349 in your handbook!

DIRECTIONS: In the following paragraph, use apostrophes to make as many contractions as you can. The first one has been made for you.

Jessica *doesn't* ~~does not~~ like to sit in class on warm spring days. She would

rather be out playing baseball with Jose and Jennifer. They are all baseball

nuts. They will spend all summer playing baseball, I am sure.

Jessica always says it is too nice to be inside, even if it is

raining. I like baseball, too, but I do not want to play in the

rain. On rainy days, I would rather play computer games.

DIRECTIONS: In this paragraph, add apostrophes where they are needed to form possessives. The first one has been done for you. (You will add six apostrophes.)

From the age of 11, Clara Barton's goal was to be a nurse. Her brothers

illness showed her that she liked to help sick people. Later, with her fathers

permission, she went to help soldiers in the Civil War. Often she stood by a

doctors side as bullets whizzed by. At the wars end, she joined the

International Red Cross. Later Barton crossed the Atlantic to help feed

Russias starving people during a famine. Clara Barton will always be

remembered for her unselfish devotion to the worlds people.

Using Apostrophes 1

The Next Step ● Use the possessive form of each of the following words in interesting or entertaining sentences. (See page 349 for help.)

1. handbook

_____

_____

_____

2. desk

_____

_____

_____

3. Mr. or Ms. _____ (your principal's name)

_____

_____

_____

4. _____ (your name)

_____

_____

_____

Using Apostrophes 2

The First Step ● Think of this exercise as advanced **apostrophe** practice. To get ready, review page 349 in your handbook.

DIRECTIONS: Add apostrophes as needed in the sentences below. You'll use them to punctuate contractions, possessives, and plurals; and in place of numbers and letters.

1. The zippers inventor was a man named Whitcomb Judson.

2. Judsons idea was to use zippers to fasten boots.

3. But in 1918, the Navy used Judsons invention to fasten flight suits.

4. It wasnt called a zipper until 26.

5. The name "zipper" stuck in peoples minds, and soon zippers were everywhere.

6. The submarines inventor was David Bushnell, an American.

7. He built the first sub, but he didnt ride in it!

8. He didnt know whether it would work.

9. The first subs mission was to attack a British ship in 1776.

10. The sub, called the *Turtle*, wasnt able to sink the ship.

11. Most people know about the Wright brothers invention, the airplane.

12. It took off in 1903, but the first helicopter didnt fly until 1907.

13. Blaise Pascals famous invention is the calculator.

14. You might say that a calculator is an invention that has its +s and −s.

Using Apostrophes 2

The Next Step ● Review the inventions listed in the handbook (pages 430-439). Write about one of these inventions in a paragraph. Use at least two possessives and two contractions. (Have a classmate check your work.)

_____

_____

_____

_____

_____

_____

_____

_____

_____

_____

_____

_____

_____

Using Quotation Marks 1

The First Step ● What do **quotation marks** mark? They mark the exact words a person speaks. They are also used to mark the titles of songs, poems, short stories, articles, etc. (See page 350 in your handbook for more information about quotation marks.)

DIRECTIONS: Add quotation marks where they are needed in the following sentences. The first two sentences have been marked for you.

1. Ricardo said, "I'm going to the library. Do you want to come?"

2. "No," I answered. "But will you check out a book for me?"

3. Sure, Ricardo said. What book do you want?

4. I asked him to bring me any book that included Edgar Allen Poe's poem called The Raven.

5. That's a great poem, Ricardo said. He asked me if I had read any of his other poems, such as The Bells and Annabel Lee.

6. I told him I hadn't read any of Poe's poems yet, but I had to read The Raven for class.

7. No problem. I'm sure I can find it, he said. Do you want anything else?

8. No, thanks, I said. If Poe's poems are like his short stories, I'll be too scared to read anything else!

The Next Step ● Re-create a conversation you and a friend have had about school, sports, books or movies. Be sure to use quotation marks correctly.

Using Quotation Marks 2

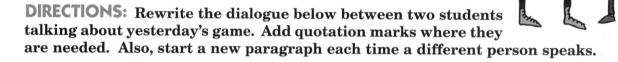

The First Step ● **Quotation marks** are used to set off dialogue. (See handbook page 350 and the student model "The Vacation" on page 165.)

DIRECTIONS: Rewrite the dialogue below between two students talking about yesterday's game. Add quotation marks where they are needed. Also, start a new paragraph each time a different person speaks.

Did you see the game yesterday? Rodrigo shouted as he jogged up the steps leading to the art room. Yeah, wasn't it great! Maria shouted back. I didn't think we had a chance. I mean, two goals to zero with only two minutes . . . ! I know! Rodrigo interrupted. I switched the channel twice before I realized what was happening. What a rally! Now it's the semifinals against Brazil, whispered Maria as they headed for their seats in the front row.

_____

_____

_____

_____

_____

_____

_____

_____

_____

_____

_____

Using Quotation Marks 3

The First Step ● **Quotation marks** are used in exactly the same way when quoting written or spoken words. (See handbook page 350, topic numbers 49-50.)

DIRECTIONS: Below are some quotes from famous books. Add quotation marks where they are needed. The first one has been done for you.

1. In *A Christmas Carol*, Charles Dickens wrote, "Scrooge looked about him for the ghost, and saw it not."

2. Rip's story was soon told, for the whole 20 years had been to him but as one night, wrote Washington Irving in "Rip Van Winkle."

3. Mark Twain wrote, in *The Adventures of Huckleberry Finn*, We went to a clump of bushes, and Tom made everybody swear to keep the secret, and then showed them a hole in the hill, right in the thickest part of the bushes.

4. At last he heard along the road at the foot of the hill the clatter of a horse's galloping hoofs, wrote Stephen Crane in *The Red Badge of Courage*.

5. In "The Legend of Sleepy Hollow," Washington Irving wrote, The night grew darker and darker; the stars seemed to sink deeper in the sky, and driving clouds occasionally hid them from his sight.

Using Quotation Marks 3

The Next Step ● Choose one of your favorite books or stories. Write a paragraph in which you quote at least one sentence from the book or story. Be sure to punctuate the quote correctly!

_____

_____

_____

_____

_____

_____

_____

_____

_____

_____

_____

_____

Punctuating Titles

The First Step ● When you include a **title** in your writing, how do you punctuate it? The general rule is that titles of complete works (such as books) are italicized, while titles of parts of works (such as book chapters) are put in quotation marks.

Page 350 in your handbook (topic number 52) explains which titles need quotation marks. Page 351 (topic number 58) explains which titles should be italicized.

DIRECTIONS: In the following sentences, put quotation marks around the titles that need them, and underline the titles that should be in italic type. The first sentence has been done for you.

1. "Too Many Cats!" is a story in a book called Cat Tales.

2. The Lion King and Aladdin are Disney movies.

3. Our science book has chapters called The Planets and Beyond and Rivers and Seas.

4. Part of a poem called The New Colossus by Emma Lazarus is written on the Statue of Liberty.

5. Little Richard sings Old MacDonald on his kids' album called Shake It All About.

6. Mom likes to watch The Simpsons.

7. My dad reads two newspapers, the Atlanta Constitution and the Wall Street Journal, plus Time magazine.

Punctuating Titles

The Next Step ● Write five sentences, each one including one of the following titles: your favorite song, album, TV show, movie, and book. Punctuate the titles correctly.

1. (song)

_____

_____

2. (album)

_____

_____

3. (TV show)

_____

_____

4. (movie)

_____

_____

5. (book)

_____

_____

Using Italics and Parentheses

The First Step ● **Italics** and **parentheses** are explained on page 351 in your handbook. This activity gives you some practice using these special punctuation marks.

DIRECTIONS: In the following sentences, underline all titles that should be in italics, and add parentheses where they are needed. The first sentence has been marked for you.

1. Washington Irving wrote a book of stories called <u>The Sketch Book</u>. Rip Van Winkle he's the guy who slept for 20 years is a character in one of Irving's stories.

2. Phillis Wheatley was a slave she was brought to America when she was about seven and never went to school. But she wrote poetry that was published in The London Magazine.

3. James Fenimore Cooper wrote both stories one book of stories is called The Leather-Stocking Tales and novels. His novel The Last of the Mohicans was made into a movie.

4. Early American writers created a new kind of story, the tall tale, about larger-than-life heroes Paul Bunyan and Pecos Bill are examples .

5. Louisa May Alcott wrote a book about her family it's called Little Women and became a favorite author of many young readers.

Using Italics and Parentheses

The Next Step ● Write sentences for each of the titles listed below. Use parentheses at least once in each sentence. Also make sure to underline words that should be in italics.

1. *Writers Express* (book)

_____

_____

_____

2. *The Lion King* (movie)

_____

_____

_____

3. *Guinness Book of Records* (book)

_____

_____

_____

4. *Sports Illustrated for Kids* (magazine)

_____

_____

_____

Punctuation Review

The First Step ● This paragraph uses almost all the different kinds of punctuation you've practiced so far. Use "Marking Punctuation" on pages 343-351 in your handbook to help you.

DIRECTIONS: Punctuation marks are missing from each of the following sentences. Correct the sentences by adding commas, apostrophes, semicolons, hyphens, and end punctuation. The first sentence has been marked for you.

The game of Monopoly is popular now, but it didn't start out that way. Charles Darrow, the inventor, tried to sell the game to Parker Brothers Company but they didnt want to buy it Parker Brothers said Darrows game took too long to play, had mistakes in the instructions and wouldnt sell Darrow had a few Monopoly games made and he paid for them himself Monopoly became very popular so Parker Brothers decided to buy it after all Monopoly became the best selling game of all time more Monopoly money than real money is printed every year How do you think Charles Darrow would have felt about this

Punctuation Review

The Next Step ● Write a paragraph about your favorite game. Explain why you like the game, why you are good at it, and so on. Trade paragraphs with a classmate when you are done. Carefully check each other's work for punctuation.

Capitalization 1

The First Step ● You already know that the first letter of a sentence is always **capitalized**. And you probably know that proper nouns are capitalized. But, uh, what's a proper noun? Glad you asked. This activity gives you practice with proper nouns.

DIRECTIONS: Your handbook explains the rules for capitalization on pages 352-354. Use topic numbers 63, 65, 67, and 71 to find and change the words that should be capitalized. The first sentence has been marked for you.

1. Gustavo and I went with dad to meet governor flood.
   ^{D} ^{G} ^{F}

2. He came to our town to give a speech about mayor frost.

3. We live in ragener, south carolina.

4. The governor doesn't come here very often, dad says, but mayor frost is a friend of his.

5. So, he came from the capital city, columbia, to give a speech in honor of the mayor.

6. According to mom, governor flood would go all the way to mars for mayor frost.

7. According to dad, the governor would rather go to washington, dc, than to mars.

8. He thinks governor flood wants to be president someday.

Capitalization 1

The Next Step ● Write a paragraph about a speech, game, concert, or other event you have attended. (Or, write about one you'd *like* to attend!) Include as much information as you can about when and where it was; what well-known people, teams, or performers you saw; etc. Be sure to capitalize correctly!

_____

_____

_____

_____

_____

_____

_____

_____

_____

_____

_____

_____

_____

Capitalization 2

The First Step ● Your handbook lists 14 different rules for **capitalization**. (See pages 352-354.) That's a lot of rules to learn! In this activity, most of the practice is on topic numbers 68, 70, 75, and 76. But you'll need to use a few others, too.

DIRECTIONS: Each of the following sentences contains two or more capitalization errors. Some words and phrases that *should* be capitalized are not; some words and phrases that *should not* be capitalized are. Make the needed corrections. The first sentence has been done for you.

1. My grandfather fought in the ~~K~~orean ~~W~~ar and in ~~W~~orld ~~W~~ar II.

2. In history class, we're studying the revolutionary war and the first

    President of the United States.

3. The league of nations was replaced by the united nations.

4. I've seen the California angels play Baseball in Anaheim Stadium.

5. The most common religion in japan is buddhism.

6. Our puerto rican neighbors speak spanish at home.

7. Most people prefer either coca-cola or pepsi soft drinks.

8. Jay got a McDonald's Hamburger and burger king fries.

9. Jonathan is jewish, and his family celebrates hanukkah.

10. Jamila, who is from kenya, knows how to speak swahili.

11. The Flintstones lived in the stone age, and the Jetsons lived in the

    space age.

Capitalization 2

The Next Step ● Choose any four of the rules for capitalization shown on handbook page 353. Then write four sentences. Each one of your sentences should use a different rule, but don't capitalize any words in your sentences. Trade with a partner, and correct each other's sentences. Write down the numbers of the rules you used to make the corrections.

Using Plurals

The First Step ● Page 355 in your handbook explains **plurals** and the rules for making them. Open your handbook to that page and do this activity.

DIRECTIONS: Change each word into its plural form. Use the rules explained in topic numbers 78, 79, and 82 in your handbook.

1. guess _____

2. potato _____

3. puppy _____

4. lunch _____

5. tomato _____

6. candy _____

7. bush _____

8. piano _____

9. key _____

10. box _____

The Next Step ● Now develop a "Found Poem," using as many of these words and their plural forms as possible. (See the model on page 204 in your handbook.)

_____

_____

_____

_____

_____

_____

_____

Using Numbers

The First Step ● This activity gives you practice using **numbers** in your writing. Page 356 in your handbook explains the rules for when to write numbers as numerals and when to write them as words.

DIRECTIONS: In the sentences below, all the numbers are written as words. Some of them should be written as numerals. Open your handbook to page 356. Using the rules in topic numbers 85, 87, and 88, find the numbers that should be written as numerals, and change them.

1. There are eleven parts in the school play.

2. We also need about ten people to sing in the chorus.

3. In the play, there are kids who are five and fifteen years old; all the other parts are for adults.

4. Three people are needed to make costumes, and all thirty of us involved with the play will sell tickets.

5. If we sell tickets for three dollars each, we'll have to sell fifty tickets to pay for the costumes.

6. We could sell popcorn for one dollar, if two people will agree to sell it.

7. We plan to give the play on February six, seven, and eight at seven p.m.

The Next Step ● Write two sentences that use numbers written correctly as numerals, and two sentences that use numbers written correctly as words.

Using Abbreviations

The First Step ● An **abbreviation** is a shorter way to write a word or phrase—a shortcut! Pages 356 and 357 in your handbook explain abbreviations and give examples.

DIRECTIONS: Below are some abbreviations that are often used in writing addresses and times. Match each abbreviation to the word or phrase it stands for.

_____ 1. St. a. ante meridiem (before noon)

_____ 2. Ave. b. Drive

_____ 3. Rd. c. Street

_____ 4. a.m. d. South

_____ 5. p.m. e. post meridiem (after noon)

_____ 6. Dr. f. Avenue

_____ 7. S. g. Road

DIRECTIONS: Below are some other common abbreviations. Match each abbreviation to the word or phrase it stands for.

_____ 1. lb a. Doctor of Medicine

_____ 2. oz b. pound

_____ 3. etc. c. paid

_____ 4. pd. d. ounce

_____ 5. M.D. e. Missus

_____ 6. Ms. f. combination of Miss and Missus

_____ 7. Mrs. g. et cetera (and so forth)

Using Abbreviations

The Next Step ● Now choose any four of the abbreviations from the matching lists and use them in sentences. You may use more than one abbreviation in a sentence.

Becoming a Better Speller

The First Step ● Making up sayings and acrostics can help you remember the spellings of difficult words. (See the bottom half of handbook page 271 for examples.)

DIRECTIONS: Try writing sayings or acrostics for four words from your spelling dictionary, or choose words that give you trouble from the list beginning on page 358. The first one has been done as an example.

1. *Their, there, and they're all begin with "the."*

2.

3.

4.

5.

Becoming a Better Speller

The Next Step ● Share your sayings and acrostics with your group. Choose the best examples of each and write them below. (Your group might also make a spelling poster with the best sayings and acrostics on it.)

_____

_____

_____

_____

_____

_____

_____

_____

_____

_____

_____

_____

_____

Using the Right Word 1

The First Step ● Your handbook lists many of the words that are commonly misused in writing. (See pages 362-369.) Use this section to help you complete this workshop activity.

DIRECTIONS: Carefully read the following story. If an underlined word is incorrect, cross it out and write the correct form above it. If the underlined word is correct, leave it alone. The first two have been corrected for you. (Work on this activity with a partner if your teacher allows it.)

In 1849, the Riker family left ~~there~~ *their* home in the East to start a ~~knew~~ *new* life in Oregon. Most pioneers traveled with other families because <u>their</u> was safety in numbers. But Janette Riker, her <u>too</u> brothers, and their father <u>choose</u> to make the trip alone.

<u>One</u> day, when they were in Montana, the men went hunting. They never came back. Janette was left alone in the wilderness. She <u>new</u> she would <u>dye</u> if she tried to cross the Rocky Mountains <u>by</u> herself.

Since cold <u>whether</u> was coming, Janette built a hut and chopped wood <u>four</u> a fire. She even killed an ox <u>so</u> she would have <u>meet</u>. She <u>herd</u> wolves and mountain lions sniffing at the door at <u>knight</u>. Can you imagine spending <u>weak</u> after <u>weak</u> alone in a tiny hut, <u>weighting</u> for spring?

When winter had <u>past</u>, Indians found Janette and <u>lead</u> her to Oregon. They were surprised that she lived <u>threw</u> the winter!

Using the Right Word 1

The Next Step ● Here's your chance to see how well you understand the word pairs you just studied. Use the following pairs correctly in sentences. The first one has been done for you.

1. their, there

   Their new car is parked over there.

   _____

2. new, knew

   _____

   _____

3. choose, chose

   _____

   _____

4. passed, past

   _____

   _____

5. led, lead

   _____

   _____

Using the Right Word 2

The First Step ● Your handbook lists many of the words that are commonly misused in writing. (See pages 362-369.) Use this section to help you complete this workshop activity.

DIRECTIONS: If an underlined word is incorrect, cross it out and write the correct form above it. If the underlined word is correct, leave it alone. The first two have been corrected for you.

When settlers from Europe came to America, they had ~~alot~~ *a lot* to learn.

There were ~~know~~ *no* stores where they could <u>by</u> things. They had to <u>rays</u> crops

and hunt for food. Native Americans <u>new</u> all about the land and the animals,

<u>sew</u> they <u>taught</u> the settlers about their new country.

Native Americans <u>learned</u> the settlers to catch fish from the rivers and

<u>creaks</u>. They told the settlers that when they planted corn, they should put a

small fish in the <u>whole</u> with the seeds. It didn't make any sense to the

settlers, but they tried it anyway. It worked! The corn plants produced more

ears of corn. The settlers also <u>learned</u> to hunt for <u>dear</u> and other animals.

They didn't <u>waste</u> anything: they <u>eight</u> the meat and used the <u>fir</u> to make

warm <u>close</u>.

America was full of things that the settlers had not <u>seen</u> in the <u>passed</u>.

They had never seen a <u>heard</u> of buffalo or <u>a</u> eagle or eaten peanuts or

cranberries. America <u>seamed</u> like a whole new world to them.

Using the Right Word 2

The Next Step ● Now test yourself by writing five sentences about some of the other things the European settlers learned when they came to America. Use the words listed below in each sentence. The first one has been done for you.

1. raise

   The settlers learned to raise many new crops.

2. learned

   _____

   _____

3. creak

   _____

   _____

4. seam

   _____

   _____

5. heard

   _____

   _____

Using the Right Word 3

The First Step ● Your handbook lists many of the words that are commonly misused in writing. (See pages 362-369.) Use this section to help you complete this workshop activity.

DIRECTIONS: If an underlined word is incorrect, cross it out and write the correct form above it. If the underlined word is correct, leave it alone. The first underlined word has been corrected for you.

The first Chinese immigrants came ~~too~~ *to* America in the mid-1800's. They were gold <u>minors</u> in California. Soon, more Chinese people came to cook and wash <u>clothes</u> for the miners. And about 10,000 Chinese men helped build <u>an</u> railroad that crossed the country from east to west.

At first, the Chinese were <u>excepted</u>. But many miners didn't <u>fined</u> gold. And <u>sum</u> people blamed the Chinese. When times get tough, <u>its</u> easy to blame people who are "new" or "different." Chinese men wore their <u>hare</u> in long braids, spoke a different language, and <u>eight</u> different food <u>than</u> other Americans. A few people wanted the Chinese and other immigrants to leave <u>there</u> new country because of such differences.

Many Chinese people stayed in America rather <u>then</u> give in to narrow-minded people. Today, <u>they're</u> part of <u>hour</u> nation, along with people from every other country in the world.

Using the Right Word 3

The Next Step ● Write sentences in which you use each of the following words correctly. Exchange your sentences with a partner and check each other's work.

1. past

_____

_____

2. minors

_____

_____

3. than

_____

_____

4. their

_____

_____

5. through

_____

_____

Changing Sentence Beginnings

The First Step ● When you polish your writing, one thing to check is how your sentences start. If they all start the same way, your writing will be boring. Read **Change Your Sentence Beginnings** on page 51 in your handbook for ideas.

UGH!

DIRECTIONS: In the following paragraph, all the sentences start exactly the same way. Using the ideas you found in your handbook, rewrite the paragraph so that most of the sentences have different beginnings. (You can leave one or two the way they are.) The first sentence has been rewritten for you as an example.

Evan leaves a trail of trouble even when he isn't trying. Evan and I were painting pictures at the kitchen table the last time I baby-sat for him. Evan painted a couple of monster faces, and then decided he wanted to do something else. Evan even offered to help clean up, which surprised me a little. Evan was carrying the bowl full of dirty water from our paintbrushes when disaster struck. Evan tripped right in front of the sink in the utility room, and the dirty water went flying. Evan will never be allowed to help again, I reminded myself as I worked.

Even when he isn't trying, Evan leaves a trail of trouble.

_____

_____

_____

_____

_____

The Next Step ● Turn to page 63 in your handbook and read the model narrative paragraph. How is your rewritten paragraph different? Which do you like better?

Using Powerful Words

The First Step ● Let's face it, some words are more interesting than others. For example, "slam" packs more punch than "close." Why? Because it tells you more!

Interesting words are one Texas-size step toward interesting writing. On page 52 in your handbook, you'll find more about using **power-packed words**.

DIRECTIONS: Rewrite the following sentences, replacing the underlined words with more powerful words or phrases. If you have trouble coming up with words, ask yourself: What kind of person or thing was it? What did it look like, or sound like, or taste like? How did the action happen? Be creative! The first sentence has been done for you.

1. I <u>told</u> the <u>dog</u> to stop <u>biting</u> on my <u>shoes</u>!

   I screamed at the Doberman to stop chomping on my tennis shoes!

2. That dog was <u>dumb</u>.

   _____

3. The door <u>came</u> open, and a <u>man</u> <u>walked</u> in.

   _____

4. Sam <u>ate</u> his <u>food</u> and <u>left</u>.

   _____

5. The <u>big</u> <u>trees</u> cast <u>big</u>, <u>dark</u> shadows.

   _____

6. The <u>cookies</u> tasted <u>good</u>.

   _____

7. My sister <u>drove</u> Dad's <u>car</u> into a ditch.

   _____

8. Someone sent my mom some <u>pretty</u> <u>flowers</u>.

   _____

Simple Subjects and Simple Verbs

The First Step ● What are the two basic parts that every sentence must have? Right: a subject and a verb. Your handbook explains them on pages 86 and 371.

DIRECTIONS: Open your handbook to page 125. Look at the model newspaper story, "Jaws!" The last paragraph has five sentences. Find the subject in each sentence. Then rewrite the sentences, changing the subject. The new subject can be anything you choose, as long as it makes a correct sentence. The first sentence has been done for you as an example.

Important Note: The last two sentences are compound sentences, so they each have two subjects. In each sentence, pick just *one* of the two subjects to change.

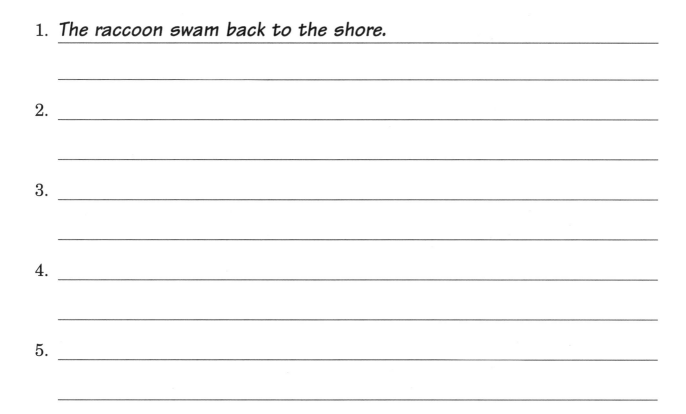

1. *The raccoon swam back to the shore.*

   _____

2. _____

   _____

3. _____

   _____

4. _____

   _____

5. _____

   _____

Simple Subjects and Simple Verbs

The Next Step ● Now, go back to the original five sentences in your handbook, and rewrite them again. This time change the verb instead of the subject. In the last two sentences, pick one of the two verbs to change. One sentence has been done for you.

1. _____

_____

_____

2. _____

_____

3. *He felt quite embarrassed.* _____

_____

4. _____

_____

5. _____

_____

Fixing Fragments 1

The First Step ● Your handbook explains different kinds of sentence errors and how to correct them. (See handbook page 87.) This activity gives you practice correcting one kind of sentence error, **sentence fragments**.

DIRECTIONS: On each line below, put an **S** if the words that follow make a sentence, or an **F** if they are a fragment. For each fragment, figure out what is missing—the subject or the verb—and write that word on the line to the right of the fragment. The first fragment has been marked for you.

__F__ 1. a baby alligator to our science class _____ *verb* _____

____ 2. brought it from the zoo _____

____ 3. it was only about one foot long _____

____ 4. named her Alice _____

____ 5. was afraid of the alligator _____

____ 6. Alice afraid of him, too _____

____ 7. next week the zookeeper will bring another animal _____

____ 8. our teacher animals _____

© Great Source. All rights reserved.

Understanding Sentences **51**

Fixing Fragments 1

The Next Step ● Go back to the fragments on page 51, and make them into complete sentences. Add a subject or a verb, whichever is needed. Use correct capitalization and punctuation. The first one has been done for you.

1. *A baby alligator <u>came</u> to our science class.*

2. _____

3. _____

4. _____

5. _____

6. _____

Fixing Fragments 2

The First Step ● This activity gives you practice correcting **sentence fragments**.

DIRECTIONS: On each line below, put an **S** if the words that follow make a sentence. Put an **F** if they are a fragment. For each fragment, figure out what is missing—the subject or the verb—and write that word on the line to the right of the fragment. The first one has been done for you.

  F   1. Franklin Roosevelt president from 1933 to 1945   *verb*

        2. was elected four times   _____

        3. but he did a lot of other things, too   _____

        4. once, he and his friends sailed to an island   _____

        5. went there to find buried treasure   _____

        6. didn't find any treasure   _____

        7. Roosevelt something else, though   _____

        8. found a nest with four baby birds in it   _____

        9. he became an avid bird-watcher   _____

Fixing Fragments 2

The Next Step ● Go back to the fragments on page 53 and make them into complete sentences. Add a subject or a verb, whichever is needed. Use correct capitalization and punctuation.

1. Franklin Roosevelt <u>was</u> president from 1933 to 1945.

2. _____

_____

3. _____

_____

4. _____

_____

5. _____

_____

6. _____

_____

Correcting Run-On Sentences 1

The First Step ● Your handbook explains a kind of sentence error called **run-on sentences**. (See page 87.) Here are two ways to correct run-on sentences: You can add end punctuation to split the run-on sentence into two sentences; or you can add punctuation and a connecting word to make one correct sentence.

DIRECTIONS: Correct the run-on sentences below by dividing them into two sentences. Use correct capitalization and end punctuation in your new sentences. If the sentence is not a run-on sentence, put a check mark next to it. The first sentence has been corrected for you.

_____ 1. Mark Twain wrote *Tom Sawyer* and *Huckleberry Finn*. He is one
                of America's most famous authors.

_____ 2. He was born in Missouri he traveled all over the world.

_____ 3. Before he became a writer, Twain was a riverboat pilot.

_____ 4. He worked on steamboats on the Mississippi River until the
                Civil War started and the river was blockaded.

_____ 5. Twain was also a silver miner in Nevada he was a
                newspaper reporter, too.

_____ 6. Later, he lived in Hartford, Connecticut, with his wife and kids.

_____ 7. Mark Twain's real name was Samuel Clemens Mark Twain was
                a "pen name."

The Next Step ● Now correct all the run-on sentences above using a comma and a connecting word (*and, so, but, yet*). For example:
1. *Mark Twain wrote <u>Tom Sawyer</u> and <u>Huckleberry Finn</u>, and he is one of America's most famous authors.*

Correcting Run-On Sentences 2

The First Step ● In this activity, you'll practice correcting **run-on sentences** by adding a comma and a connecting word to make one correct sentence.

DIRECTIONS: Correct the run-on sentences below by adding a comma and a connecting word (*and, so, but, yet*). If the sentence is not a run-on sentence, put a check mark next to it. The first sentence has been corrected for you.

_____ 1. Anna Moses was a famous artist_∧ _, but_ she didn't begin painting until she was 78 years old.

_____ 2. She enjoyed painting scenes near her farm in New York she often gave away her paintings.

_____ 3. One day an art collector saw her paintings in a store window he liked them very much.

_____ 4. He went to her home and bought every painting she had—15 of them!

_____ 5. Three of those paintings ended up in the Museum of Modern Art Anna Moses was a big success.

_____ 6. Her style of painting was called American Primitive she became famous even in Europe.

_____ 7. She was known as Grandma Moses and lived to be 101.

The Next Step ● Which of the above run-on sentences could be corrected using a semicolon instead of a comma and a connecting word? See topic number 25 on page 347 in your handbook for more information on semicolons.

Correcting Rambling Sentences

The First Step ● Your handbook explains different kinds of sentence errors and how to correct them. (See handbook page 87.) This activity gives you practice correcting one kind of sentence error, **rambling sentences**.

DIRECTIONS: Below are two rambling sentences. Correct them by dividing them into as many sentences as you think are needed. Cross out the extra *and*'s, capitalize the first word of each sentence, and use the correct end punctuation. The first sentence has been done for you.

1. Our class went to the art museum; and a man who worked there gave us a special tour; and he told us about all the artists and when they lived and he told us that one artist named Vincent van Gogh cut off his own ear and Raul asked why and our guide said that nobody knew for sure and Raul thinks that van Gogh must have been nuts.

2. Maria's mom owns a restaurant called Old Mexico and it's near our school and Maria's mom invited our whole class to come to the restaurant for lunch and our teacher said that we could go so we went today and we all got to have anything we wanted and almost everybody had two desserts and it was great!

Correcting Rambling Sentences

The Next Step ● You and a classmate each write a rambling sentence. (See how long you can make it!) Then trade and correct each other's sentences.

_____

_____

_____

_____

_____

_____

_____

_____

_____

_____

_____

_____

Subject-Verb Agreement 1

> **The First Step** ● One basic rule of writing sentences is that the subject and verb must "agree." Sentence agreement is explained on page 88 in your handbook.

DIRECTIONS: Check the following sentences for subject-verb agreement. If the sentence is correct, put a check mark in front of it. If the subject and verb do not agree, correct the verb. An example has been done for you.

_____ 1. Americans speaks more than 100 different languages.

_____ 2. Many people moves to the United States from other countries.

_____ 3. They bring their languages with them.

_____ 4. Most immigrants comes from Mexico, Vietnam, and the Philippines.

_____ 5. My friend Annie speak Tagalog.

_____ 6. She is from the Philippines.

_____ 7. Jorge and Marta speaks Spanish.

_____ 8. English and Spanish are the most common languages in the United States.

_____ 9. Some native-born Americans speaks languages besides English.

_____ 10. For example, Native Americans has their own languages.

_____ 11. My aunt is from Hawaii.

_____ 12. She know both Hawaiian and English.

Subject-Verb Agreement 2

The First Step ● Making subjects and verbs agree can be harder when the sentence has a compound subject. Review the material about compound subjects on page 88 in your handbook.

DIRECTIONS: In some of the following sentences, the subject and verb do not agree. Correct the verbs in those sentences. Put a check mark in front of the sentences that are correct. The first sentence has been done for you.

_____ 1. My mother or sisters asks me questions in Spanish.

_____ 2. Ricki and Rhoda takes me to the movies.

_____ 3. The teacher or the principal make the announcements.

_____ 4. The first baseman or the shortstop bat first.

_____ 5. My brothers and their dog go to the park.

_____ 6. Rick or his sisters takes the trash out.

_____ 7. My family and my school recycles paper.

_____ 8. My mom or my sisters drive me to school.

_____ 9. My sisters or my mom drive me to school.

_____ 10. Several cars or a bus take us on field trips.

The Next Step ● Using one of the sentences above as a starting point, write a short, funny story. Use as many compound subjects as you can, but be sure that your verbs always agree. Refer to page 88 in your handbook to check your writing. (Write your story on your own paper.)

Sentence Problems

The First Step ● Page 89 in your handbook explains four common kinds of **sentence problems**. Review them. Which ones sometimes creep into your sentences?

DIRECTIONS: Most of the following sentences contain sentence problems. Correct them by crossing out or changing the word that is incorrect. If the sentence is correct, make a check on the blank in front of it. The first sentence has been done for you.

_____ 1. People who move to the United States from other countries t~~hey~~ are called immigrants.

_____ 2. If there had been no immigrants, there wouldn't be nobody in the United States except Native Americans.

_____ 3. The United States was once considered a melting pot, blending many cultures into one.

_____ 4. My friend and her father arrived two years ago from India, and he will be happy to become U.S. citizens.

_____ 5. Some people say immigrants should of stayed in the countries they came from.

_____ 6. But that doesn't make no sense.

_____ 7. Most of us we are either immigrants or descendants of immigrants.

Sentence Problems

The Next Step ● Decide which kind of sentence problem is the biggest problem *for you*. Choose a partner, and ask your partner to write a few sentences that contain that sentence problem. Meanwhile, you write a few sentences that contain your partner's biggest sentence problem! Trade papers, and correct each other's sentences.

_____

_____

_____

_____

_____

_____

_____

_____

_____

_____

_____

_____

_____

Combining Sentences 1

The First Step ● Pages 91 and 92 in your handbook explain ways to **combine sentences** using words and phrases. Review those pages; then do this practice activity.

DIRECTIONS: Combine the following pairs of sentences into one sentence using the methods on pages 91 and 92. The words in parentheses tell you which method to use. The first sentence has been done for you.

1. Pizza is cheesy. Pizza is gooey. Pizza is great. (series of words)

    Pizza is cheesy, gooey, and great.

2. Susan is tall. Susan is skinny. Susan is a fast runner. (series of words)

3. At camp we play baseball. We jump on a trampoline. (compound verb)

4. Marcia goes to the lake. She swims to the buoy and back. (compound verb)

5. Sue won a golf tournament. She is my writing partner. (appositive phrase)

6. Todd got the Frisbee. He got it off the roof. (prepositional phrase)

7. Karen got a new bike. It's a 12-speed. (key word)

Understanding Sentences **63**

Combining Sentences 2

The First Step ● One way to **combine sentences** is to make complex sentences. You connect two ideas with a subordinate conjunction. Your handbook explains complex sentences on page 93.

DIRECTIONS: Combine the following pairs of sentences to make complex sentences. Be sure to use a subordinate conjunction as explained in your handbook on page 387. The first one has been done for you.

1. Millions of Jewish people left Russia. They faced prejudice there.

   Millions of Jewish people left Russia because they faced prejudice

   there.

2. People from Great Britain found it easy to adjust to the United States. They already spoke English.

   _____

   _____

3. Most Irish immigrants came during the 1800's. There was a famine in Ireland.

   _____

   _____

4. Many people from Sweden settled in Minnesota. They knew how to farm in cold weather.

   _____

   _____

The Next Step ● Write a complex sentence using a subordinate conjunction that you did not use in the sentences above.

Combining Sentences 3

The First Step ● One way to **combine sentences** is to make complex sentences. You may combine two ideas using a relative pronoun. Your handbook explains this on page 93. For more information about relative pronouns, see page 379.

DIRECTIONS: Combine the following pairs of sentences to make complex sentences. Use relative pronouns as explained in your handbook. The first one has been done for you.

1. Greek immigrants often opened restaurants in the United States. They had been farmers in Greece.

   Greek immigrants, who had been farmers in Greece, often opened

   restaurants in the United States.

2. Most Italian immigrants settled near other Italians. They had strong family ties.

   _____

   _____

3. The Vietnam War resulted in many Vietnamese people coming to the United States. The war ended in 1975.

   _____

   _____

   _____

4. African-Americans make up about 12 percent of Americans. African-Americans' ancestors were often brought here as slaves.

   _____

   _____

   _____

Combining Sentences 4

The First Step ● You've already had some practice **combining sentences**. You've seen how sentence combining can make your writing smoother and more interesting. Now review pages 90-93 in your handbook and get ready for a challenge!

DIRECTIONS: Rewrite the following paragraphs on the lines below. Combine short, choppy sentences to make smooth ones. Combine them however you choose, as long as the meaning stays the same and your sentences are correct.

There was a barn. It was dusty. It was made of wood. The wood was old. The wood was gray. The nails marked their age. They showed signs of permanent rust. There was an old silo. It stood next to the barn. It looked queer. It was every bit as old as the barn.

Just then, Penny appeared. She appeared in front of the barn. The animals looked up at her. They were surprised. Penny never came into the barnyard. Not at this time of day.

_____

_____

_____

_____

_____

_____

The Next Step ● Turn to page 154 in your handbook. Read the first two paragraphs of "Montgomery Mews Mysteriously." How do they compare to your paragraphs?

Making Compound Sentences

The First Step ● This workshop activity gives you practice combining sentences by making **compound sentences**. See page 93 of your handbook for information about compound sentences.

DIRECTIONS: Combine the following pairs of sentences into one compound sentence. Remember, use a comma and words such as *and, but, so,* or *for* to make compound sentences. The first sentence has been done for you.

1. I know three kids from other countries. I like them.

   I know three kids from other countries, and I like them.

2. Two of them are from Mexico. One is from India.

   _____

3. They have different holidays. It's interesting to learn about them.

   _____

   _____

4. In Mexico, they have Cinco de Mayo. In India, they have Divali.

   _____

   _____

5. I don't speak Spanish or Marathi. My friends speak English.

   _____

   _____

Making Compound Sentences

The Next Step ● Write a paragraph or short story about a holiday or custom your family observes. After you've finished, go back and check your sentences. Should any of your short sentences be combined into compound sentences? If so, change them before you exchange your stories.

_____

_____

_____

_____

_____

_____

_____

_____

_____

_____

_____

_____

_____

_____

Types of Sentences 1

The First Step ● Read about **simple**, **compound**, and **complex sentences** on page 373 in your handbook. If you're not sure you understand how to tell the three types of sentences apart, turn to pages 91-93. All the model sentences on pages 91-92 are simple sentences. Compound and complex sentences are modeled on page 93.

DIRECTIONS: Here is part of the model book review of *The True Confessions of Charlotte Doyle* on page 133 in your handbook. On the lines below, write *simple*, *compound*, or *complex* to identify each sentence. The hardest sentence has been done for you!

1. The True Confessions of Charlotte Doyle is about a wealthy thirteen-year-old girl named Charlotte. _____

2. In 1832, Charlotte is supposed to sail from England to Rhode Island with two other families, but the families never show up. _____

3. Charlotte decides to sail with the crew alone. _____

4. She becomes good friends with the captain, until the captain kills two of the crewmen for being traitors. _____

5. Charlotte then decides to join the crew and becomes "Mr. Doyle" in the logbook. _____

6. During a storm, the first mate, Hollybrass, is killed with her knife! _____

7. I think Avi, the author, wanted to tell his readers that even people like Charlotte who are very shy can become strong and brave. *complex*

8. She had to make many hard choices. _____

9. I think he also wanted readers to understand that accusations aren't always true. _____

10. I liked the book because Avi made all the characters seem real. _____

Types of Sentences 2

The First Step ● Review the **types of sentences** on page 373 in your handbook before doing this practice activity. You may also want to read about clauses on page 372 and review the information about compound and complex sentences on page 93.

DIRECTIONS: Rewrite each of the following simple sentences twice. First add an independent clause (that is, another simple sentence) to make a compound sentence. Then add a dependent clause to make a complex sentence. An example has been done for you.

1. My brother has a new set of skates.

    compound: *My brother has a new set of skates, and he uses them*

    every day.

    complex: *My brother has a new set of skates that he uses every day.*

2. Her school has a computer club.

    compound: _____

    _____

    complex: _____

    _____

3. My dad cooks Italian food.

    compound: _____

    _____

    complex: _____

    _____

4. Our teacher travels every summer.

    compound: _____

    _____

    complex: _____

    _____

Simple and Compound Sentences

The First Step ● Recall as much as possible about **simple** and **compound sentences**. Then turn to page 373 in your handbook and carefully reread the section on simple and compound sentences.

Examples:

Simple Sentences

My sisters wanted to earn money for camp.
They decided to wash cars for $3.00 each.

Compound Sentence

My sisters wanted to earn money for camp,
so they decided to wash cars for $3.00 each.

DIRECTIONS: **Think of a time you did something to earn money. Write four simple sentences about your experience. Then combine the sentences so you have two compound sentences. Check the coordinate conjunctions on page 387, and try to use a different one for each sentence. (See page 93 for more on compound sentences.)**

Simple Sentences

1. _____

2. _____

3. _____

4. _____

Compound Sentences

1. _____

_____

2. _____

_____

The Next Step ● Check your compound sentences for proper punctuation. Did you use a comma before a conjunction? Or did you simply use a semicolon? What about end punctuation?

Kinds of Sentences

The First Step ● There are four kinds of sentences: **declarative**, **interrogative**, **imperative**, and **exclamatory**. Turn to page 373 in your handbook, and read the section about the four kinds of sentences.

Examples:

Declarative

The John Hancock Building and the Empire State Building are famous skyscrapers.

Interrogative

How many states can you see from the top of these buildings?

Imperative

You must go to the top.

Exclamatory

The people look like ants!

DIRECTIONS: Recall a time you had an awesome experience. Maybe you went to the top of a skyscraper, got stuck on the top of a Ferris wheel, or rode a dirt bike for the first time. Write one sentence of each kind about your experience.

Declarative _____

_____

Interrogative _____

_____

Imperative _____

_____

Exclamatory _____

_____

Parts of Speech Review

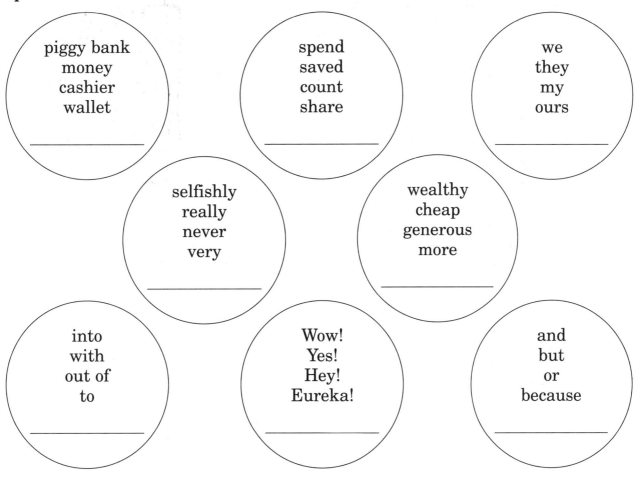

The First Step ● Each of the **eight parts of speech** is important, but some words are more meaningful than others. We think that nouns carry the most meaning. See what you think when you finish this page.

DIRECTIONS: Identify the part of speech for each list of words by writing it on the line in the circle. See page 374 in your handbook for a list of the eight parts of speech.

piggy bank
money
cashier
wallet
_____

spend
saved
count
share
_____

we
they
my
ours
_____

selfishly
really
never
very
_____

wealthy
cheap
generous
more
_____

into
with
out of
to
_____

Wow!
Yes!
Hey!
Eureka!
_____

and
but
or
because
_____

The Next Step ● Now write a sentence using as many of the parts of speech as you can. You may want to use some of the words in the circles.

_____

_____

_____

Identifying Common and Proper Nouns

The First Step ● Nouns can be labeled as **common** or **proper**. Check your handbook if you need an explanation of these terms. (See handbook page 375.)

DIRECTIONS: Underline each noun in the sentences below; then write **C** above each common noun and **P** above each proper noun. (The number of nouns in each sentence has been given in parentheses.)

       P

Juan bought a bike from Green's, a hardware store in his neighborhood. (5)

He bought a secondhand Schwinn bike, and it seemed to be in very good

condition. (2) He bought the bike on Saturday, rode it around on Sunday, but

on Monday the handlebars started wobbling. (5) On Tuesday, he took his

Schwinn bike back to the store and told Mr. Green, the owner, about the

handlebars. (6) Mr. Green got out his wrench and a couple bolts and fixed the

handlebars right away! (4) Now Juan thinks his secondhand bike is better

than all the new bikes at Green's. (4)

The Next Step ● Look around you and notice all the persons, places, things, and ideas. Then make two lists—one of proper nouns and one of common nouns. See how many you can spot!

Proper Nouns	Common Nouns

Uses of Nouns

The First Step ● Nouns can be used in different ways in sentences. You've had lots of practice using **subject nouns**, which are nouns used as the subject of a sentence. But you also need to know how to use **predicate nouns** and **possessive nouns**. Read about all three uses on page 376 in your handbook.

DIRECTIONS: In the sentences below, label all the underlined nouns. Write an **S** above the noun if it is a subject noun, a **P** if it is a predicate noun, and a **POS** if it is a possessive noun. The first sentence has been done for you.

1. A (S) <u>beagle</u> is a friendly (P) <u>dog</u>.

2. The <u>party</u> will be a <u>surprise</u>.

3. <u>Jeremy's</u> <u>cat</u> is a <u>Siamese</u>.

4. <u>Marla's</u> favorite <u>sport</u> is <u>baseball</u>.

5. <u>Jordan</u> became an <u>artist</u>.

6. The <u>winner</u> was <u>Suzanne</u>.

7. <u>Blake</u> knows <u>Lydia's</u> brother.

8. The <u>book's</u> <u>author</u> signed my copy.

9. Our <u>school's</u> track <u>team</u> won the championship.

10. My best hiding <u>place</u> is the <u>attic</u>.

The Next Step ● Fill in each blank below with a predicate noun.

1. The laziest color is _____ .

2. My worst day is _____ .

3. The best sport is _____ .

4. My favorite animal is the _____ .

Nouns As Objects

The First Step ● A noun is a **direct object** when it receives the action of the verb. A noun is an **indirect object** when it names the person to or for whom something is done. A noun is an **object of a preposition** when it is part of a prepositional phrase.

DIRECTIONS: Look at the following sentences and the circled nouns in each. Then label each noun according to which kind of object it is. (Use page 376 in your handbook as a guide.)

Yelena wrote a funny (letter.) _____

Yelena wrote (Mike) a funny letter. _____

Yelena wrote a funny letter to (Mike.) _____

DIRECTIONS: Now write three sentences on your own. Each one should contain a noun used as a different kind of object. Your sentences may contain more than one kind of object. *Special Challenge:* You may want to write with compound objects just the way you write with compound subjects. Check out this example:

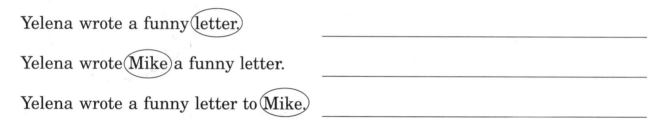

(direct object)
Yelena wrote a funny **letter** to **Mike** and **Maggie**.
(compound object of a preposition)

1. _____

   _____

2. _____

   _____

3. _____

   _____

The Next Step ● When you're finished, exchange your work with a classmate. Find and label the nouns used as objects. Did your partner write at least one example of each?

Pronouns

The First Step ● Read about "Person of a Pronoun" on page 378 in your handbook. The **person of a pronoun** indicates the point of view of a story. The activities below will help you explore different points of view.

Examples from *Cinderella*:

First-Person Point of View
  I cleaned and scrubbed the cottage all day.

Second-Person Point of View
  You two will go to the ball to meet the prince.

Third-Person Point of View
  She had to leave the ball by midnight.

DIRECTIONS: Write a different ending to *Cinderella*. Write it from the first-person or third-person point of view. Circle five pronouns in your story. Are most of them in the same person?

_____

_____

_____

_____

_____

_____

_____

_____

The Next Step ● In a small group, share your story endings and decide which point of view was used in each of them.

Person of a Pronoun

> **The First Step** ● Review the lists of personal pronouns in your handbook (page 377), and also the section on **Person of a Pronoun** (page 378).

DIRECTIONS: In the following sentences, underline the personal pronouns. Above each pronoun, write a 1, 2, or 3 to show whether it is a first-person pronoun, second-person pronoun, or third-person pronoun. The first two sentences have been done for you.

1. ③She likes ①me, and ①I like ③her.

2. Do ②you want to play volleyball with ①us?

3. I made lemonade, and they built a sand castle.

4. They built a moat around it.

5. Where did you and he go?

6. Do you and she want to come with me?

7. You should ride his bike.

8. They don't know where her car is.

9. He borrowed a bike from her because she wasn't going to use it.

10. You can return it to us or to them.

11. Is my bike in your car or in their car?

Types of Verbs

The First Step ● Review **Types of Verbs** on page 380 in your handbook before you do this activity.

DIRECTIONS: Read the following sentences and look at the underlined verbs. Decide whether the verbs are action verbs (A), linking verbs (L), or helping verbs (H). Write the correct letter above each. The first one has been done for you.

1. Rolf, our bulldog, <u>loves</u> ⒜ doggy biscuits.

2. Those biscuits must <u>taste</u> ◯ good, because he <u>hides</u> ◯ them everywhere.

3. Then he <u>can</u> ◯ <u>snack</u> ◯ anytime.

4. I <u>have</u> ◯ <u>found</u> ◯ biscuits in my shoes.

5. Dad <u>has</u> ◯ <u>spotted</u> ◯ biscuits under his chewed-up gloves.

6. Rolf <u>chews</u> ◯ gloves, too . . . and socks.

7. Oh, yes, and Rolf <u>sneaks</u> ◯ cookies, but only the fresh-baked kind.

8. Our family <u>has</u> ◯ <u>grown</u> ◯ fond of Rolf, though.

9. At least he <u>smells</u> ◯ sweet.

10. Rolf always <u>spills</u> ◯ my bath powder on his way through the bathroom.

Types of Verbs

The Next Step ● Pretend that you have a new pen pal.
Write a letter in which you introduce yourself; tell about your
life, family, and friends; and ask your pen pal about his or her
life.   After you finish, go back and underline all the verbs in
your letter, and label each one as an action verb (A), a
linking verb (L), or a helping verb (H).

Using Irregular Verbs

The First Step ● **Irregular verbs** don't play by the rules! When you make them past tense, you can't just add "ed" as you do with regular verbs. The only way to learn the past tense and past participles of irregular verbs is to memorize each one. And that takes practice.

DIRECTIONS: Study the chart of irregular verbs on page 382 in your handbook. Then close your handbook and fill in the missing words in the chart below.

present tense	past tense	past participle
1. blow		*blown*
2. bring		*brought*
3. draw		
4. eat	*ate*	
5. fly		
6. hang		*hung*
7. hide	*hid*	
8. know		
9. lay (to put in place)		
10. lie (to lie down)	*lay*	
11. run		*run*
12. see	*saw*	

The Next Step ● Now check your work. Turn to the chart on page 382 and look up each word you filled in. Make a list of all the verbs you got wrong, and write sentences using each one. (If you didn't make any mistakes, choose any two verbs and write sentences using them.)

Irregular Verbs

The First Step ● **Irregular verbs** are not normal! When you change them to past tense or use them with a helping verb, they change in different ways. The only way to know how they change is to learn the different forms of each verb.

DIRECTIONS: Fill in the chart below to see how well you know the different forms for nine common irregular verbs. The first one has been done for you.

Present Tense	Past Tense	Past Participle
see	*saw*	seen
	wrote	
drive		
		frozen
	burst	
begin		
		blown
	gave	
speak		

The Next Step ● Now check your work. Turn to the chart on page 382 and look up each word you filled in. Make a list of all the verbs you got wrong, and write a sentence using each one.

The Tense of a Verb

The First Step ● The **present tense** of a verb states an action that is happening now, or that happens regularly. The **past tense** of a verb states an action that happened at a specific time in the past. The **future tense** of a verb states an action that will take place. (See handbook page 383.)

Examples:

Present Tense	The cricket, mouse, and cat **enjoy** talking to each other.
Past Tense	They **pranced** about the newsstand half the night.
Future Tense	The three characters **will win** the hearts of their readers.

DIRECTIONS: These three sentences are about the gentle animals in *Cricket in Times Square* by George Sheldon. Now *you* write some sentences about imaginary animals that you have read about or seen in a cartoon. Write at least two sentences for each of the tenses.

Present Tense Sentences: _____

_____

_____

_____

Past Tense Sentences: _____

_____

_____

_____

Future Tense Sentences: _____

_____

_____

_____

The Tense of a Verb

Adjectives

The First Step ● An **adjective** is a word that describes a noun or a pronoun. Adjectives are used in both the subject and predicate part of the sentence. (See handbook page 384.)

DIRECTIONS: Write four adjectives to describe each of the different moods pictured below.

The Next Step ● Let's say the dog's name is Chester. Write an acrostic poem, using adjectives to describe him. You may use some of the adjectives above, and you may need to think of some new ones.

C _____

H _____

E _____

S _____

T _____

E _____

R _____

All About Adjectives and You

The First Step ● Turn to page 384 in your handbook and read about the **comparative** and **superlative** forms of adjectives. Also check the "Special Forms" section on that page.

Examples of some special forms of adjectives:

Sam is the **best** keyboard player in the class.

He is even **better** than his teacher.

He knows **more** songs by heart than anyone else.

DIRECTIONS: Write about something that you can do very well. (This is a chance to boast about yourself a little!) Use as many comparative and superlative forms of adjectives as possible. Underline your adjectives.

The Next Step ● Share your writing with a partner. After you've read about each other's talents, label all the comparative and superlative adjectives.

All About Adverbs

The First Step ● Most **adverbs** tell where, how, or when. They describe a verb, an adjective, or another adverb. See page 385 in your handbook for more about adverbs.

DIRECTIONS: In each of the following sentences, circle the adverb and draw a line to the word it describes. On the line next to the sentence, write whether the adverb tells where, how, or when. The first two sentences have been done for you.

1. Jody and I often go to the park.   *when*

2. Sometimes we play softball.   *when*

3. We choose our teams carefully.   _____

4. We play hard and play to win.   _____

5. Jody and I always pitch.   _____

6. Tasha never strikes out.   _____

7. Ira hits the ball hard.   _____

8. Most fielders step back for Ira.   _____

9. Monica easily catches ground balls.   _____

DIRECTIONS: In each of the following sentences, add an adverb that answers the question in parentheses. Write the new sentence on the line. Then, circle the adverb and draw a line to the word it describes. The first one has been done for you.

I'm going to the park.   (when)   *I'm going to the park later.*

Marcia eats.   (how)   _____

Rodrigo laughs.   (how)   _____

Let's go swimming.   (when)   _____

All About Adverbs

_____

_____

_____

_____

_____

_____

_____

_____

_____

_____

_____

_____

Forms of Adverbs

The First Step ● Review page 385 in your handbook. Then do this activity to practice using the different forms of **adverbs**.

DIRECTIONS: Rewrite each sentence below two times. In your first sentence, use the comparative form of the underlined adverb. In your second sentence, use the superlative form of the same adverb. An example has been done for you.

1. Gabriella runs <u>fast</u>.

   Bev runs faster than Sarah.

   Teri runs fastest of all.

2. Bruce played <u>well</u>.

   _____

   _____

3. Larissa plays her CD's <u>loudly</u>.

   _____

   _____

4. Terrence reads <u>slowly</u>.

   _____

   _____

5. Spot panted <u>eagerly</u>.

   _____

   _____

Forms of Adverbs

The Next Step ● Think of three adverbs that describe *how* something is done. Then write sentences using the positive, comparative, and superlative forms of each adverb. A sample has been done for you.

1. adverb = *carefully*

   Jim writes his stories carefully.

   Rosa writes hers more carefully than Jim.

   Clare writes hers most carefully of all.

2. adverb = _____

   _____

   _____

   _____

3. adverb = _____

   _____

   _____

   _____

4. adverb = _____

   _____

   _____

   _____

Prepositions

The First Step ● Turn to page 386 in your handbook and review the information about **prepositional phrases**.

Examples:

I went **to a concert** this summer.

I sat **in the first row.**

DIRECTIONS: Pretend that you really did go to a concert. Write a friendly letter telling one of your best friends about it. Describe what you did. Put parentheses around the prepositional phrases you use in your letter.

M·m·m·m·m·m·

Dear _____ ,

The Next Step ● Try reading your letter and leaving out all of the prepositional phrases. What happens?

Your friend,

Interjections

The First Step ● An **interjection** is a word or phrase used to express strong emotions or surprise. A comma or an exclamation point is used to separate an interjection from the rest of the sentence. (See page 387 in your handbook.)

Examples:

Wow! Does it bite?

Hey! I think you better hold him now!

Man! I wouldn't do that!

Yikes! Let her have the first turn!

DIRECTIONS: Pretend you just spent some time with a herpetologist (someone who works with snakes and other reptiles). Write a postcard telling a friend how you felt about being around snakes. Did you hold the snake, or did you just watch? Use interjections to let your friend know how strongly you felt about this experience.

_____ , 199 ____

Dear _____ ,

_____

_____   _____

_____   _____

_____   _____

_____

From,

_____

Using Conjunctions

The First Step ● Conjunctions are words that connect words, phrases, or clauses. Your handbook explains conjunctions on page 387. In this activity, you'll practice using all three kinds of conjunctions: coordinate conjunctions, subordinate conjunctions, and correlative conjunctions.

DIRECTIONS: Connect each group of words below to make one sentence, using a conjunction. Check your handbook to first decide which of the three kinds of conjunctions to use. Then choose the best conjunction. A few examples have been done for you.

1. Marci brought cake to class. Marci brought ice cream to class.

   Marci brought cake and ice cream to class. (coordinate)

2. Jason got the flu. He played football in the rain.

   Jason got the flu after he played football in the rain. (subordinate)

3. Our teacher may lead the assembly. Our principal may lead the assembly.

4. Yelena got a new haircut. She doesn't like it.

5. Josh wanted to come. He had a cold.

6. My dog got sick. He ate a whole box of cookies.

Coordinate Conjunctions

The First Step ● **Coordinate conjunctions** connect equal parts. For example, coordinate conjunctions can connect two words, two phrases, or two clauses. (See page 387 in your handbook.)

DIRECTIONS: Use one of the coordinate conjunctions listed in the box to fill in the blank in each sentence below.

and	but	or	so	yet

1. My dog Harold is small _____ strong.

2. He has white paws _____ shaggy ears.

3. All afternoon he sleeps on the porch _____ in the house.

4. When I get home, he wants to run _____ play.

5. Harold is fat _____ fast.

DIRECTIONS: Coordinate conjunctions can be used to connect two simple sentences and make a compound sentence. (Pages 86 and 373 in your handbook explain compound sentences.) Use a comma, plus a coordinate conjunction from the box above, to connect each pair of simple sentences below.

1. Harold loves dog food. He loves people food, too.

_____

2. I give Harold cookies. He's always happy to see me.

_____

3. He likes hamburgers. He's not supposed to have them.

_____

4. Harold loves bones. He looks for them in grocery bags.

_____

Subordinate Conjunctions

> **The First Step** ● Use a **subordinate conjunction** to connect two clauses to make a complex sentence. (See page 387 in your handbook.)

DIRECTIONS: Choose subordinate conjunctions from the list in the box below and write them on the lines to complete the story.

> **after, although, as if, because, before, if, in order that, since, so, that, though, unless, until, when, where, while**

We were in art class _____ our principal reminded everyone that the dress rehearsal before the concert would begin at 6:00 p.m., sharp! _____ Matt arrived just five minutes before the concert, Mr. Martin, the choir director, told him that he would have to miss out on the party. _____ the concert was over, Matt raced off the bleachers and disappeared. We spotted him using the office phone. We were surprised to see Matt at the party later _____ he explained his reason for being late. Matt's new brother had just been born!

Subordinate Conjunctions

The Next Step ● Now write your own school-related story. Use a variety of subordinate conjunctions to make at least three complex sentences. Hint: You may begin a complex sentence with a subordinate conjunction.

_____

_____

_____

_____

_____

_____

_____

_____

_____

_____

_____

_____

_____

_____

_____

Minilessons

The minilessons in this section of your SourceBook cover basic editing and proofreading skills. All the minilessons are cross-referenced with your handbook.

Marking Punctuation Minilessons

Double Up . . . . *Using Semicolons*

READ about semicolons on **page 347** in your handbook. Then WRITE three compound sentences, using semicolons to COMBINE the simple sentences (also called independent clauses) below.

I'm going to the zoo tomorrow.

That's the best place to see the fireworks.

The reptile house is what I want to see.

I'll have chocolate chip.

The ice-cream truck has lots of flavors.

We're going to the city park on the Fourth of July.

1. _____

_____

2. _____

_____

3. _____

_____

Next WRITE two simple sentences of your own.

1. _____

2. _____

Then USE a semicolon to combine your two simple sentences into one sentence.

1. _____

_____

A Worm-Digging Experience . . . . *Hyphens*

FILL IN the blanks with hyphenated adjectives formed from the list of words below. See handbook **page 348** for help. The first one has been done for you.

1. My _____*worm-digging*_____ brother makes big bucks selling bait!

2. That _____ cat brings its prey home. Yuck!

3. The plate held my _____ lunch.

4. Take a picture of those _____ mountains.

5. The _____ mystery story kept me awake.

digging   half   loving   pounding   covered

mouse   worm   tree   eaten   heart

I told her not to—BANG!—slam the door. . . . . *Dashes*

To each of the following sentences, ADD a word or phrase that needs to be set off with a dash. Remember, dashes set off a quick change in direction, or an interruption in the flow of thought. An example has been done for you. (See **page 348** in your handbook.)

1. The baseball landed right in the potato salad.

The baseball landed—plop!—right in the potato salad.

2. The dog barked and ran out the door.

_____

3. I finally finished my chores and went swimming.

_____

4. I cut my hand on the sharp metal can.

_____

5. She went to Jody's. She went to Angie's.

_____

Shorten it! . . . . *Contractions*

MAKE CONTRACTIONS from the following phrases. If you need help, check
page 349 in your handbook. To check your work, look up your contractions
in a dictionary.

1. I will _____

2. could not _____

3. have not _____

4. she would _____

5. does not _____

6. They are _____

7. it is _____

8. Let us _____

9. cannot _____

10. should have _____

Charlie's Horse . . . . *Possessives*

LIST the names of seven people you know. Next to each name, WRITE its
possessive form. (*Hint:* You'll need seven apostrophes. See your handbook,
page 349, topic number 45, for details!)

1. _____   _____

2. _____   _____

3. _____   _____

4. _____   _____

5. _____   _____

6. _____   _____

7. _____   _____

Tell me more. . . . . *Parentheses*

To each of the following sentences, ADD a word or phrase that needs to be set off with parentheses. Remember, parentheses set off words that add information or make something clearer. An example has been done for you. Also see **page 351** in your handbook.

1. My sisters gang up on me.

   My sisters (they're twins) gang up on me.

2. My cousin is in the air force.

   _____

   _____

3. My aunt plays in an orchestra.

   _____

   _____

4. We wanted to play outdoors, but the weather was bad.

   _____

   _____

5. We didn't have enough people for a team.

   _____

   _____

Editing for Mechanics Minilessons

Name that place. . . . . *Capitalization*

Open your handbook to **page 353**, topic number 67. For each type of
    geographic name listed, LIST two more examples. Do as many as you can
    on your own; then check a map or an atlas if you need to.
SHARE your work.

1. Planets and heavenly bodies _____ _____

2. Continents _____ _____

3. Countries _____ _____

4. States _____ _____

5. Provinces _____ _____

6. Cities and counties _____ _____

7. Bodies of water _____ _____

8. Landforms _____ _____

9. Public areas _____ _____

10. Roads and highways _____ _____

11. Buildings _____ _____

To Cap or Not to Cap . . . . *Capitalization*

The following words are sometimes capitalized. It depends on how the word is
    used in the sentence. (See handbook **pages 352-354**.)
WRITE two sentences using each word: one sentence in which the word is
    capitalized, and one in which it is not. (*One more thing:* Do not use the
    words as first words in your sentences!)

mother   north   white house
president   earth   war

Puppies on the Loose . . . . *Plurals*

IMAGINE that your dog has six puppies. One day while you're at school, the
puppies romp through the house, destroying everything in sight.
WRITE a short story about the puppies' day, using the plural forms of as many
of the following words as you can. (See handbook **page 355**.)

shoe	dish	tomato	guppy
sofa	box	turkey	paw
pillow	candy	loaf	nose

Zip Zap . . . . *Abbreviations*

See **page 146** of your handbook for help in changing the addresses below into
the form preferred by the United States Postal Service. See **page 357** for
abbreviations of the underlined words.

MS MAURA ANTHONY

2635 NORTH PINE STREET

AUGUSTA MAINE 10000

_____

_____

_____

MR FELIX UNGER

PRESIDENT

FOOTBALL FANS OF AMERICA

BOX 42

BUFFALO NEW YORK 14213

_____

_____

_____

_____

Then WRITE your name and address and the address of a friend or relative in
the same form.

Don't MTB; it's PN! .... *Initialisms*

THINK of at least five phrases that you use all the time—"no way," "pizza night," "home before dark," "miss the bus," etc.

TURN all your phrases into initialisms. (Into what? Check your handbook, **page 356**, topic number 91.)

For Example: "miss the bus" becomes MTB; "pizza night" becomes PN.

Now WRITE a paragraph using all your initialisms.

TRADE paragraphs with a partner.

FIGURE OUT each other's initialisms. What do they stand for?

Checking Your Spelling Minilessons

Short, but Not Always Simple .... *Check Your Spelling*

Just because a word is short does not mean it is easy to spell. There may be a
letter that you do not hear when you pronounce the word, or a sound that
could be spelled several different ways.

LOOK for 10 three- or four-letter words in the list of commonly misspelled
words on **pages 358-361** in your handbook. CHOOSE ones that cause you
trouble, and write them down.

TALK about why each one might be easy to misspell.

WRITE a brief paragraph that uses as many of these short words as possible.
UNDERLINE each short word that you used from your list.

ASK a partner to read your paragraph and check the spellings of your
underlined words, using the list of commonly misspelled words.

Just add "ly." .... *Check Your Spelling*

Just by adding "ly" to many adjectives, you can change them into adverbs. See
pages 384-385 in your handbook for more information on adjectives and
adverbs.

LIST all of the adverbs (formed by adding "ly" to an adjective) that you find in
the list of commonly misspelled words on **pages 358-361** in your handbook.

(*Note:* Which word drops a final "e" before adding "ly"? _____)

1. _____   6. _____

2. _____   7. _____

3. _____   8. _____

4. _____   9. _____

5. _____   10. _____

FIND four words in the list that you could change from adjectives to adverbs
just by adding "ly."

11. _____   13. _____

12. _____   14.

Using the Right Word Minilessons

REWRITE each of the following sentences, using *can* or *may* (or *cannot* or *may not*) to REPLACE the underlined words. (See handbook **page 363**.)

1. I <u>am not able to</u> juggle four bananas at one time.

   _____

2. I <u>am not allowed to</u> juggle bananas in the living room.

   _____

3. My dog <u>knows how to</u> fetch.

   _____

4. He also knows that he <u>is not allowed to</u> go into the living room.

   _____

   _____

5. My mother said I <u>am free to</u> go to the movies.

   _____

6. But I don't think I <u>will be able to</u> stay up that late.

   _____

7. My dog <u>doesn't know how to</u> read or write.

   _____

8. But he still <u>gets to</u> go to school on Pet Day.

   _____

Flash the Fish .... *Usage: "Its" or "It's"?*

FILL IN the blanks in the sentences below, using "its" or "it's," whichever is correct. Check **page 365** of your handbook for help.

1. _____ time to give the goldfish _____ food.

2. _____ name is Flash, and _____ a small goldfish.

3. It swims around in _____ bowl, waiting for _____ dinner.

4. _____ too bad Flash can't go anywhere.

5. But _____ safer for a goldfish to stay in _____ bowl.

6. When you're a goldfish, _____ a big, dry world out there.

Who's on first? .... *Usage: "Whose" or "Who's"?*

FILL IN the blanks in the sentences below, using "whose" or "who's," whichever is correct. Check **page 369** of your handbook for help.

1. _____ book is this?

2. It belongs to Jordan, _____ in my math class.

3. _____ going to the recycling center?

4. _____ turn is it to go?

5. This is Sanjeev, _____ family is from India.

6. Is he the one _____ new here?

7. _____ science class are you in?

8. My teacher is Ms. Chang, _____ from China.

Understanding Sentences Minilessons

Then I heard . . . . *Kinds of Sentences*

IMAGINE yourself at a beach or pool in the summertime. People are
swimming, diving, splashing, wading, talking, yelling, and laughing.
WRITE down at least eight sentences that you might overhear. Then READ
each sentence and IDENTIFY the kinds of sentences you have written.
(The four kinds of sentences are declarative, interrogative, imperative, and
exclamatory.) Is one kind of sentence more common than another?
SHARE your work with another student.

Patchwork Stories . . . . *Sentence Fragments*

MAKE UP five sentence fragments. (See **page 87** in your handbook for an
explanation of fragments.) Imagine that you will use them to write a
story—make them as colorful and interesting as you can. Make sure some
of the fragments need a subject, and some need a verb.
TRADE with a partner who has done the same thing. Turn each other's
fragments into sentences that make a story. Your sentences can be funny
or weird—as long as they're correct!

Says who? . . . . *Sentence Fragments*

Although sentence fragments are errors in your writing (see your handbook,
page 87), they're okay in your talking! People use fragments all the time
when they talk to each other:

"Going to the mall?"

"No money."

"Basketball?"

"Too cold."

WRITE a short conversation between two people. Make everything they say a
fragment.
Then REWRITE each piece of dialogue as a complete sentence.

In Your Own Words . . . . *Run-On Sentences*

TURN to **page 87** in your handbook and read the section on run-on sentences.
REWRITE the section in your own words: First write a sentence that explains
what a run-on sentence is. Then make up your own example of a run-on.
Then, show two ways to correct it.

Newswriting . . . . *Run-On Sentences*

FIND a very short article (two or three paragraphs) in a newspaper.
COPY the article, but combine several pairs of sentences to make run-on
sentences. (See **page 87** in your handbook for an example.)
Now, TRADE papers with a classmate who has done the same thing. Correct
each other's article. Try to use both ways of correcting run-ons that are
explained on page 87.
Finally, COMPARE your corrected article to the original article. How is it
different?

And so on, and so on . . . . *Rambling Sentences*

FIND a very short news article (two or three paragraphs) in a newspaper.
COPY the article onto a sheet of paper, leaving out all the end punctuation
and initial capital letters. Add the word "and" in each place where a
sentence ended. In other words, make the article into one long, rambling
sentence.
Now TRADE papers with a classmate who has done the same thing.
CORRECT each other's rambling sentences. If you need help, see **page 87**
in your handbook.
Finally, COMPARE your corrected sentences with the original article. Your
sentences don't have to match the article exactly, as long as they are correct
and the meaning is clear.

Get it together. . . . . *Combining Sentences*

COMBINE each of the following pairs of sentences into one sentence. After each new sentence, write which rule for combining sentences you used. (The rules are listed and explained on **pages 90-93** in your handbook.) One example is shown below.

1. Marcy sent some valentines. Mark sent some valentines. *Marcy and Mark sent some valentines. (Use a compound subject.)*

2. The movie was long. The movie made me cry. _____

3. Rahim got a new bike. It is red. _____

4. My mother runs marathons. My mother swims laps. _____

5. My parents are going to France. I'm not going with them. _____

6. My parents are flying to France. They're flying on a wide-body jet. _____

Understanding Our Language Minilessons

What am I? . . . . *Identifying Concrete Nouns*

COMPOSE "What Am I" riddles about 2-3 objects in your classroom.

Example: *I have a mouth and silver teeth that fall out everywhere. What am I? (answer: Stapler)*

SHARE your riddles with a classmate and listen to his or hers.

LIST all the riddle answers on the lines below. (See handbook **page 375** for an explanation of abstract and concrete nouns.) LABEL each noun "abstract" or "concrete." What have you discovered?

_____   _____

_____   _____

_____   _____

_____   _____

_____   _____

_____   _____

Just My Type . . . . *Uses of Nouns*

READ the essay "Why My Family Recycles Newspapers" on **page 76** in your
handbook. Then USE **page 376** in your handbook to help you.

LABEL the 10 nouns in the first paragraph of the essay. The first one is done
for you.

1. *family (object of preposition)*

2.

3.

4.

5.

6.

7.

8.

9.

10.

Special Challenge: WRITE your own sentences about recycling. EXCHANGE
sentences with a partner and LABEL each noun.

Family Reunion . . . . *Relative Pronouns*

READ about relative pronouns on **page 379** in your handbook.

FIND the list of relative pronouns.

WRITE two or three sentences about one of your favorite relatives.

USE relative pronouns to help you share some interesting details about your
cousin, uncle, grandmother, aunt, etc. You can have fun with this exercise;
however, you don't want to embarrass anyone!

Mirror Image . . . . *Intensive and Reflexive Pronouns*

Intensive and reflexive pronouns work like mirrors in a sentence. See **page 379** in your handbook for examples and a list of intensive and reflexive pronouns.

CHOOSE one of the pronouns listed.

WRITE two sentences: one in which the pronoun is intensive and one in which it is reflexive.

ASK yourself what noun or pronoun your intensive or reflexive pronoun refers to in each sentence.

Special Challenge: TAKE turns reading your sentences for the class.

Lost and Found . . . . *Person of a Pronoun*

LIST all of the things you might find in the school's lost-and-found department.

CHOOSE two or three of these items and give them an opportunity to tell how they feel about being in the lost-and-found.

USE the first-person plural point of view. (That means you will be using the word *we* quite often.) See **page 378** of your handbook.

Name-Dropper . . . . *Using Irregular Verbs*

REVIEW the list of irregular verbs in your handbook on **page 382**.

FIND two irregular verbs that begin with the first letter in your first or last name. (If that doesn't work, use the name of a friend or family member.)

WRITE three crazy sentences for each verb by completing the sentence starters below. (Make sure that you use the correct form of the verb.)

1. *Yesterday, I* _____

_____

2. *I have* _____

_____

3. *I will* _____

_____

Sentence Ladder 1 . . . . *Adjectives*

START a sentence ladder with the following pattern.

The | spotted | dog waited in the | warm | car.
| *little* | | *yellow* |

WRITE the above sentence on your paper.

THINK OF as many adjectives as possible to replace those in the boxes.

WRITE the replacements in a row of boxes under the adjectives "spotted" and "warm." (Keep going as long as you can.) SHARE your results with a partner.

Sentence Ladder 2 . . . . *Adverbs*

CREATE a sentence ladder by changing the adverb as many times as you can in each of the following sentences.

1. The motorcycle goes | fast. |

2. I run | ahead. |

USE different forms of the adverb when it is possible. *Example:* fast (positive), faster (comparative), fastest (superlative)

It's under the . . . , next to . . . . *Prepositions*

Have you ever had someone give you directions that sound more like a director directing an actor in a movie?

For Example: "Now go <u>into</u> the bedroom. <u>Against</u> the far wall, <u>next to</u> the window, you see the tall dresser. Open the top drawer <u>on</u> the left . . . "

WRITE specific directions for how to find something in a room at home, at school, or in another place that's very familiar to you.

As you write, USE a lot of prepositions. (See handbook **page 386.**)

TRADE papers. Can your partner visualize (see) what you're describing? The team that uses the most prepositions accurately wins!

Both . . . and . . . . *Conjunctions*

READ about correlative conjunctions in your handbook on **page 387.**

Then WRITE as many sentences as you can that use the correlative conjunctions "both, and." Here are some examples to get you started:

Both Jose *and* I can wiggle our ears.

Both girls *and* boys like to act funky.

SELECT your favorite sentences.

ARRANGE them as a poem titled "Both . . . and . . ."

CREATE a table with five spaces across and five spaces down. Down the side
WRITE five letters; across the top WRITE names of five parts of speech.
Then FILL IN the table with as many words as you can that correspond to
the letters and the parts of speech. Or, you may use the chart below.
ADD five more letters and exchange charts with a partner.
Special Challenge: THINK of ways to make this activity into a game. Or do
this as a timed activity.

	noun	adverb	preposition	verb	adjective
b	*box*	*badly*	*before*	*brushed*	*blue*
p					
d					
f					
o					

Check-It-Out Daily Sentences

The Check-It-Out Daily Sentences in this section of your SourceBook come in two different varieties. The focused sentences help you concentrate on one proofreading skill at a time. The proofreading sentences provide two or three different types of errors for you to correct.

Focused Sentences

● **End Punctuation**

Did you know there is one male calico cat for every
300,000 females

● **End Punctuation**

Heat makes you sleepy in the afternoon and restless
at night

● **End Punctuation**

Oh no, that plane is going to crash

● **End Punctuation**

Why are all the Yellow Freight Company's trucks orange

● **End Punctuation**

Watch out for that speeding car

Focused Sentences

● **Commas (In a Series)**

The languages spoken by the largest number of people are Chinese English Hindi Russian and Spanish.

● **Commas (In a Series)**

The five most popular ice-cream flavors are vanilla chocolate Neapolitan chocolate chip and strawberry.

● **Commas (In a Series)**

According to a survey of historians, the best presidents of all time are Abraham Lincoln George Washington Franklin Roosevelt Theodore Roosevelt and Thomas Jefferson.

● **Commas (In a Series)**

Have you ever noticed a red orange silver or beige tag on the back of Levi jeans?

● **Commas (In a Series)**

The word "facetiously" contains all of the vowels in the alphabet in order: <u>a</u> <u>e</u> <u>i</u> <u>o</u> <u>u</u> and <u>y</u>.

Focused Sentences

● **Commas (Between Independent Clauses)**

A "Falling Rocks" sign means you are in an area where rocks could fall but a "Fallen Rocks" sign means you should watch for rocks already on the road.

● **Commas (Between Independent Clauses)**

A "Slow Children" sign does not mean the children in the area are slow but it does mean drivers should slow down and watch carefully for children.

● **Commas (Between Independent Clauses)**

Tom and Jerry is my least favorite cartoon show so I only watch it if there's nothing else to do.

● **Commas (Between Independent Clauses)**

President Franklin Roosevelt was crippled by polio but the American public was not aware of how severe the crippling was.

● **Commas (Between Independent Clauses)**

Not even the smartest scientists can figure out how the chubby bumblebee can fly but it just goes ahead and flies anyway.

Focused Sentences

● **Commas (To Set Off Appositives)**

Hershey, Pennsylvania home of the Hershey Chocolate Company is called "Chocolate Town U.S.A."; Burlington, Wisconsin home of Nestle's Chocolate Company is called "Chocolate City U.S.A."

● **Commas (To Set Off Appositives)**

The Chicago Bears National Football League champions of 1947 played the college all-stars at Soldier Field a huge stadium in Chicago.

● **Commas (To Set Off Appositives)**

A record crowd of 112,376 football fans watched the Houston Oilers beat the Dallas Cowboys 1994 Super Bowl champions in Mexico City on August 15.

● **Commas (To Set Off Appositives)**

Paul Anderson the strongest man in the world once lifted a table with six people on top of it.

● **Commas (To Set Off Appositives)**

Paul Anderson 1956 Olympic weight lifter won a gold medal for lifting 6,270 pounds.

Focused Sentences

● **Commas (To Set Off Long Phrases and Clauses)**

Early in the 1974 baseball season Hank Aaron broke Babe Ruth's record by hitting his 715th home run.

● **Commas (To Set Off Long Phrases and Clauses)**

Even though some people think it was named after a baseball legend the Baby Ruth candy bar was actually named after President Cleveland's oldest daughter, Ruth.

● **Commas (To Set Off Long Phrases and Clauses)**

When airplane pilots fly in an easterly direction they fly at an odd-numbered altitude such as 29,000 feet.

● **Commas (To Set Off Long Phrases and Clauses)**

Flying at the even-numbered altitude of 30,000 feet we knew we were headed west.

● **Commas (To Set Off Long Phrases and Clauses)**

As the fall winds blow the last leaves from the trees the bears of northern Wisconsin begin looking for a good place to sleep.

Focused Sentences

● **Semicolon**

The United States has actually had a "King" living in the White House President Gerald Ford's birth name before he was adopted was Leslie Lynch King, Jr.

● **Semicolon**

The very first Olympic Games took place in 776 B.C. at the foot of Mt. Olympus in Greece the first modern Olympic Games were held in 1896 in Athens, Greece.

● **Semicolon**

The great Chicago fire of 1871 lasted 27 hours it destroyed 17,450 buildings and killed 250 people.

● **Semicolon**

The Chisholm Trail runs between San Antonio and Abilene many "real" cowboys herded cattle along that trail in 1871.

● **Semicolon**

Blowtorches of today can heat objects to over 14,000 degrees Fahrenheit diamonds will actually burn at that temperature!

Focused Sentences

CHECK IT OUT

● **Hyphen**

My well meaning mother makes me take some

nasty tasting cough medicine at the first sign of a cold.

● **Dash**

Captain James T. Kirk of <u>Star Trek</u> fame has an uncommon

middle name Tiberius.

● **Dash**

The first English author to receive the Nobel Prize for

literature this isn't surprising was Rudyard Kipling in 1907.

● **Hyphen**

Long playing records (you know, those old fashioned albums

your grandparents have) were invented by Peter Goldmark.

● **Dash**

In 1867, a place where poor immigrant workers labored too

hard and too long received a fitting name the sweatshop.

Focused Sentences

● **Apostrophes**

Because singer Frank Sinatras eyes are a beautiful blue color, he is called Ol Blue Eyes by his fans.

● **Apostrophes**

All of the bicycles horns out at the bike rack were broken by vandals.

● **Apostrophes**

The soft tissue of peoples vocal cords shrinks with age, making mens voices higher and womens softer.

● **Apostrophes**

Nebraskas winter winds blow hard and cold.

● **Apostrophes**

The <u>T</u>s burned into the steers hides tell you which ranch they belong to.

Focused Sentences

CHECK IT OUT

● **Quotation Marks**

Happy Birthday to You was adapted from a song by Mildred J. and Patty Hill called Good Morning to You.

● **Quotation Marks**

The landlord yelled up the stairs, Tap dancing sounds too much like a demolition derby down here! Try ballet!

● **Quotation Marks**

I think Writing Fantasies is one of the best chapters in my new handbook, and there's a lot of cool stuff in The Student Almanac, too!

● **Quotation Marks**

The phrase passing the buck was first written down by Mark Twain; it seems that poker players used to pass an object called a buck to the next dealer.

● **Quotation Marks**

The slang expression ain't dates back to King Charles II of England who used it as a substitute for am not or are not.

Focused Sentences

● **Italics (Underlining)**

The three bears from the book The Three Bears must have liked porridge.

● **Italics (Underlining)**

The Marx Brothers starred in comic movies like A Night at the Opera.

● **Italics (Underlining)**

The words do your homework do not mean "Go ahead. Watch another episode of Gilligan's Island."

● **Italics (Underlining)**

The Marshmallow's latest record, Soft Sugar, is already a big hit.

● **Italics (Underlining)**

The Spanish word hacienda means a "large estate or plantation."

Focused Sentences

● Capitalization

Mercury, the closest planet to the sun, is a little larger than earth's moon.

● Capitalization

The region of transylvania is a real place in romania.

● Capitalization

Mount everest is the highest mountain in the world, but it is only 44 feet higher than K2, which is also called mount godwin austen.

● Capitalization

The chinese language is spoken by the most people in the World, but english is the most widespread language.

● Capitalization

Brad says burger king and hardee's restaurants have the best fries on the planet, but he's never tasted the food at juicy lucy's truck stop.

Focused Sentences

● **Plurals**

The man at the corner stand sells balloones, boxs of candy, and bunchs of flowers.

● **Plurals**

Henry VIII had six wifes. One of his childs became a famous queen.

● **Plurals**

Monkies can chatter and howl, filling the jungle with echos of their noise.

● **Plurals**

Elephantes, whales, and cowes have calfs that require much care.

● **Plurals**

Soloes are played by one musician, duets by two, and trioes by three.

Focused Sentences

● **Numbers**

There are over three and a half billion chickens in the world — plenty of drumsticks to go around!

● **Numbers**

20 of my classmates made the honor roll last quarter; that's ninety percent of the class!

● **Numbers**

A female blue whale measuring one hundred and thirteen feet in length is the largest animal ever seen alive.

● **Numbers**

In nineteen ninety-three the Clinton family moved to Sixteen Hundred Pennsylvania Avenue, Washington, D.C. Two Zero Zero Zero Six.

● **Numbers**

Skip chapters four and five for now, but read pages forty and forty-one in chapter 6 for tomorrow.

Focused Sentences

● **Using the Right Word**

I've heard tails of the see's rage that would turn you're hair white!

● **Using the Right Word**

If you poor all of the lemonade into you're glass, their will be nothing left for me to drink.

● **Using the Right Word**

A storm window keeps the warm heir in you're house wear it belongs.

● **Using the Right Word**

It seams that the piccolo players always set next to the flutists in a orchestra.

● **Using the Right Word**

Little Ralphy untied all the nots he'd tied in the maid's apron strings, so she gave him a extra peace of cake afterward.

Focused Sentences

● **Combining Sentences**

The class of animals called Arachnida includes spiders.
This class includes scorpions. It includes ticks as well.

● **Combining Sentences**

The piece of amber contains a fossilized dragonfly.
The piece of amber is golden. It is on the professor's desk.

● **Combining Sentences**

The Swiss Alps are cut by many deep valleys.
The valleys contain pretty towns and villages.

● **Combining Sentences**

Greenland is the largest island on earth.
Greenland was discovered in 982 by Eric the Red.

● **Combining Sentences**

Canoeing on rivers in the spring can be dangerous.
Sudden rainstorms can cause flash flooding.

Focused Sentences

● **Subject-Verb Agreement**

An African black mamba snake have been clocked slithering at 30 miles an hour.

● **Subject-Verb Agreement**

Sidewinder rattlesnakes actually moves by jumping sideways along the ground.

● **Subject-Verb Agreement**

Either the mamba or the blue racer are poisonous, but I can't remember which one.

● **Subject-Verb Agreement**

Chocolate and vanilla remains the favorite ice-cream flavors.

● **Subject-Verb Agreement**

The highest bridge in the world were built 1,053 feet above Royal Gorge in Colorado.

Proofreading Sentences

History of the Language

- ### Using the Right Word, Numbers, Capitalization

  The oldest letter of the alphabet is the letter "O," dating back two the year three thousand b.c.

- ### Subject-Verb Agreement, Commas (In a Series)

  Our language are always changing because of the way we talk write and use words from day to day.

- ### Using the Right Word, Contractions, Double Negative

  Sum slang words used in the 1960's arent never used much anymore.

- ### Numbers, Using the Right Word, Run-On Sentence

  Calligraphy is the art of beautiful handwriting it developed into a art form more than two thousand years ago.

- ### Commas (To Set Off Appositives), Capitalization

  Latin the language of the roman Empire is the foundation of the english language.

Proofreading Sentences

Animal Crackers 1

● **Possessives, Using the Right Word**

A hummingbirds bill works like a straw four sucking nectar from a flower.

● **Plurals, Commas (In a Series)**

Certain kinds of bats cricketes and salamanderes live in caves.

● **Adjectives (Comparative), Possessives, Using the Right Word**

A giraffes neck has no more bones then a humans — the bones are simply more larger.

● **Possessives, Using the Right Word**

Parrots bills work like nutcrackers too open seeds and nuts.

● **Subject-Verb Agreement, Sentence Fragment**

Either the emu baby or the kangaroo baby are called a joey. Can't remember.

Proofreading Sentences

Animal Crackers 2

● **Commas (To Set Off Long Phrases and Clauses),
Using the Right Word**

When a horse and a donkey have a foal its called a mule.

● **Commas (Between Independent Clauses),
Using the Right Word**

The kangaroo has a long, thick tale and this helps the animal balance while leaping.

● **Irregular Verbs, Pronoun/Antecedent Agreement,
Contractions**

If you ever sawed a picture of a pike (a kind of fish), I think youd agree they look really mean.

● **Subject-Verb Agreement, Plurals, Double Negative**

There have never been no documented proof of healthy wolfs attacking human beings.

● **Hyphens, Pronoun/Antecedent Agreement,
Using the Right Word**

Two year old bears are as large as there parents when it leaves home.

Proofreading Sentences

Maps, Maps, Maps 1

● End Punctuation, Capitalization

The oldest map of the World is a clay tablet from Babylon made around 600 B.C..

● Capitalization, Using the Right Word

The base of the great pyramid of giza is a perfect square with the for sides resting on exact North-South and East-West lines.

● Commas (To Set Off Appositives), Parentheses

Mount Everest the tallest mountain in the world still grows at a rate of one centimeter that's .394 inches every year.

● Commas (To Set Off Appositives and in Dates)

On May 28 1953 Sir Edmund Hillary an explorer from New Zealand and Tenzing Norkay a guide from Nepal became the first people to reach the top of Mount Everest.

● Using the Right Word, Commas (To Set Off Long Phrases), Capitalization

According to the united states geological survey every year they're over an million little earthquakes around the world.

Proofreading Sentences

Maps, Maps, Maps 2

● **Subject-Verb Agreement, Using the Right Word**

The first true cities was the capitols of early civilizations, such as Ur in Mesopotamia.

● **Numbers, Capitalization, End Punctuation**

The pyramids of giza are one of the 7 wonders of the world do you know what the other 6 are and what they have in common.

● **Parentheses, Irregular Verbs**

American explorer Richard E. Byrd 1888-1957 becomed the first person to fly over the North Pole in 1926.

● **Commas (In Dates), Using the Right Word, Possessives**

On July 11 1969 Neil Armstrong became the first man too walk on the moons surface.

● **Subject-Verb Agreement, Possessives, Run-On Sentence**

Robert E. Peary and Roald Amundsen was the first explorers to arrive at the earth poles Peary went north in 1909, and Amundsen went south in 1911.

Proofreading Sentences

Maps, Maps, Maps 3

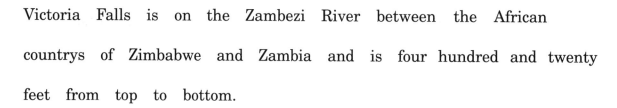

- **Plurals, Numbers**

    Victoria Falls is on the Zambezi River between the African countrys of Zimbabwe and Zambia and is four hundred and twenty feet from top to bottom.

- **Capitalization, Numbers**

    The great Barrier Reef off the Northeast coast of Australia is one thousand and two hundred miles of beautifully colored coral.

- **Capitalization, Numbers**

    The Sears tower is the tallest building in the world with one hundred and ten stories that rise almost fifteen hundred feet (four hundred and forty-three meters) above the streets of chicago.

- **Subject-Verb Agreement, Adjectives (Superlative)**

    The Uru people lives on the most high island in the world in the middle of Lake Titicaca in South America.

- **Capitalization, Using the Right Word**

    Scientists have found fish skeletons in the middle of the Sahara dessert, which indicates that once their was an ocean their.

Proofreading Sentences

Maps, Maps, Maps 4

● **Possessives, Using the Right Word**

Swedens capital city of Stockholm is built on an island attached too the mainland buy many bridges.

● **Using the Right Word, Capitalization**

The country of Brazil moved it's capitol from the coastal city of Rio de Janeiro inland to the new city of brasilia.

● **Adjectives (Superlative), Commas (To Set Off Appositives)**

The baddest criminals of England used to be sent to Tasmania an island off the coast of Australia.

● **Capitalization, Numbers, Plurals, Parallelism**

The 3 south American countrys of Guyana, Suriname, and French Guiana are north of Brazil, have port citys for capitals, and each country borders the Atlantic ocean.

● **Italics (Underlining), Capitalization**

The word "peninsula" comes from the latin paene for "almost" and insulae for "island."

Proofreading Sentences

Colors, Signs, and Symbols 1

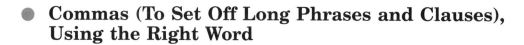

- ### Commas (To Set Off Long Phrases and Clauses), Using the Right Word

  When riding your bike extend you're left arm straight out too signal a left turn.

- ### Commas (To Set Off Long Phrases and Clauses), Subject-Verb Agreement, Using the Right Word

  To signal a write turn on your bike extend your left arm out and bends it up at the elbow with your palm forward.

- ### Subject-Verb Agreement, Using the Right Word

  The director of a television show signal that time are running out buy swirling a index finger around in a circle.

- ### Possessives, Subject-Verb Agreement

  A tap of a finger on a television directors nose indicate that the performer or announcer is right on time.

- ### Commas (To Set Off Long Phrases and Clauses), Subject-Verb Agreement

  When a television director rubs together the index finger and thumb of both hands the performer or announcer on stage are being signaled to slow down.

Proofreading Sentences

Colors, Signs, and Symbols 2

● **Possessives, Plurals, Parentheses**

The different patterns and colores of Scotlands kilts skirts represent different clans, or familys.

● **Possessives, Combining Sentences**

Brides dresses are often white. That color has symbolized joy for many years.

● **Quotation Marks, Capitalization**

Sequoyah created a written language for the cherokee people in 1821, said mrs. henning.

● **Capitalization, Commas (To Set Off Interruptions), Possessives**

Uncle sam in case you don't know was a real person whose famous picture was used on the u.s. armys enlistment posters.

● **Using the Right Word, Subject-Verb Agreement, Commas (To Set Off Appositives)**

Putting you're index finger and thumb together to make a "O" are a weigh of saying OK which means "all right."

Proofreading Sentences

● **Colon, Commas (In a Series)**

The acronym ROY G. BIV stands for each of the colors of the rainbow red orange yellow green blue indigo and violet.

● **Using the Right Word, Commas (To Set Off Interruptions)**

Ordinary white light which can be separated buy a prism is maid up of all the colors of the rainbow.

● **Commas (To Set Off Appositives), Contractions, Using the Right Word**

Ultraviolet is a light beyond violet the last color of the spectrum; ultraviolet radiation cant be scene.

● **Commas (Between Independent Clauses), Contractions, Subject-Verb Agreement**

Objects reflects different parts of the light spectrum and thats why we see colors.

● **Using the Right Word, Run-On Sentence**

A laser beam is photons of light traveling in the same direction such a beam can be powerful enough to burn a whole in medal.

Proofreading Sentences

Colors, Signs, and Symbols 4

● **Pronouns, Commas (To Separate Adjectives), Irregular Verbs**

The common everyday handshake begun when men wanted to show each other them did not have weapons in their hands.

● **Subject-Verb Agreement, Run-On Sentence**

You has to identify many traffic signs when you ride a bike the stop sign and the yield sign are two important ones.

● **Commas (In a Series), Parentheses**

The police the military the FBI Federal Bureau of Investigation and other organizations use fingerprints to identify people.

● **Capitalization, Commas (In a Series)**

In his paintings, Pablo picasso used different shapes to represent people animals things and ideas.

● **Commas (To Set Off Appositives), Capitalization, Subject-Verb Agreement**

Leonardo da Vinci one of the greatest italian painters were also interested in many areas of science.

Proofreading Sentences

U.S. History 1

● **Commas (To Set Off Long Phrases and Clauses), Capitalization**

Once the new american government was installed in 1789 George Washington was sworn in as the first President.

● **Possessives, Irregular Verbs, Capitalization**

The Civil war begun in 1861 when the Confederate's opened fire upon Fort Sumter.

● **Capitalization, Commas (In Dates)**

The civil war ended at appomattax court house on April 9 1865.

● **Irregular Verbs, Capitalization, Hyphens**

Rioting taked place when an African American student named James Meredith enrolled at the university of Mississippi in 1962.

● **Numbers, Commas (To Set Off Long Phrases and Clauses), Hyphens**

Upon entering the University of Georgia in 1962 Charlayne Hunter-Gault became the first African American student there in one hundred seventy-five years.

Proofreading Sentences

U.S. History 2

● **Possessives, Irregular Verbs**

Uncle Sams picture was first drawed by cartoonist Thomas Nast.

● **Possessives, Using the Right Word, Colon**

Thomas Nast also drew the mane political party symbols the Democrats donkey and the Republicans elephant.

● **Commas (In Addresses), Capitalization**

The first United States Congress met in princeton new jersey not in Washington D.C.

● **Capitalization, Commas (In Dates), Using the Right Word**

President Lincoln issued the emancipation proclamation on september 22 1862, and it took affect on january 1 1863.

● **Capitalization, Using the Right Word**

During the roaring twenties, women which cut there hair short and danced the Charleston were called "flappers."

Proofreading Sentences

Science and Inventions 1

● **Subject-Verb Agreement, Capitalization, Commas (To Set Off Appositives)**

Marie curie one of the first noted female scientists were born in poland in 1867.

● **Capitalization, Run-On Sentence, Abbreviations**

Elizabeth Blackwell graduated from Medical school in 1849 she was the first woman in the U.S. to earn a medical degree.

● **Colon, Capitalization, Possessives**

Scientists divide the earths history into four eras precambrian, paleozoic, mesozoic, cenozoic.

● **Subject-Verb Agreement, Possessives, Numbers**

Scientist's believe that the earth's 7 continents was once attached.

● **Quotation Marks, Commas (In a Series), Capitalization**

One definition of the word Precipitation refers to hail mist rain sleet or snow.

Proofreading Sentences

Science and Inventions 2

- ### Commas (Between Independent Clauses), Using the Right Word

  Kinetic energy is the energy of moving things and potential energy is energy who could be used.

- ### Capitalization, Possessives, Commas (In a Series)

  George washington Carver greatly helped the souths economy by improving peanuts soybeans and sweet potatoes.

- ### Subject-Verb Agreement, Using the Right Word

  Growth hormones in the write places makes it possible four a plant two bend toward the light.

- ### Run-On Sentence, Using the Right Word

  A firefly lights up when the air tubes in it's stomach are filled buy oxygen and a pigment of fat its not magic or electricity.

- ### Contractions, Using the Right Word, End Punctuation, Plurals

  Dont you think you're science teacher all ready nose that a group of monkies is a band.

Proofreading Sentences

Science and Inventions 3

● **Using the Right Word, Numbers**

   A dessert is any area of the earth that gets fewer than 1 inch of rainfall every year.

● **Commas (To Set Off Long Phrases and Clauses), Possessives, Adjectives (Comparative)**

   The farther you go below the oceans surface the more cold and saltier it gets.

● **Using the Right Word, Adverbs (Comparative)**

   Sound travels more better and more faster in water then in air because the liquid molecules are closer together.

● **Pronoun/Antecedent Agreement, Using the Right Word**

   Certain supernovas, or superstars, flare up in a big weigh; it may reach the brilliance of 200 million sons!

● **Plurals, Parallelism**

   Potatos consist mainly of starch, protein, and they have water in them.

Proofreading Sentences

Literature and Life 1

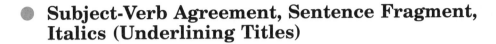

- ### Subject-Verb Agreement, Sentence Fragment, Italics (Underlining Titles)

    My friend and I wants to see the movie King Kong, a story about a big, hairy ape. Actually attacks New York City!

- ### Capitalization, Possessives

    Just tell me when we're dead and hot and cold summer are the childrens favorite books.

- ### Using the Right Word, Adjectives (Comparative), Capitalization

    Anwar and Sumo are more better names for kittens then the two most popular ones, tiger and samantha.

- ### Rambling Sentence, Numbers

    I don't want to wear mink and I could wear my wool coat instead and did you know that forty mink had to die for that coat?

- ### Pronoun/Antecedent Agreement, Commas (In Direct Address)

    Class we will write panagrams today. It is sentences that use all the letters of the alphabet.

Proofreading Sentences

Literature and Life 2

● **Capitalization, Commas (To Set Off Appositives)**

In 1933 mickey mouse received quite a few more fan letters than Shirley Temple the most popular living performer.

● **Commas (To Set Off Appositives), Possessives, Italics (Underlining Titles)**

Theodor Geisel also known as Dr. Seuss wrote the wonderful childrens books The Cat in the Hat and Green Eggs and Ham.

● **Italics (Underlining Titles), Numbers, Capitalization**

Robert louis stevenson wrote The Strange Case of dr. Jekyll and mr. Hyde in 3 days.

● **Using the Right Word, Capitalization**

Its true that mark twain liked righting in bed and produced quiet a few chapters their in pure comfort.

● **Commas (In Dates), Capitalization, Irregular Verbs**

On june 22, 1990 billy joel becomed the first Rock 'n' Roll artist to perform in Yankee Stadium.

Proofreading Sentences

Literature and Life 3

- **Using the Right Word, Numbers, Capitalization**

  If you were to poor a bowl of fruit loops, wood you get 3, four, or 5 flavors?

- **Capitalization, Using the Right Word**

  In the summer I like going too the store for breyer's ice cream and graf's root beer.

- **Italics (Underlining Titles), Capitalization, Run-On Sentence**

  You should read The Moonstone by wilkie collins its about a diamond.

- **Using the Right Word, Capitalization, Contractions**

  If you read The Chronicles of narnia, youll meat the character reepicheep.

- **Italics (Underlining Titles), Capitalization, Abbreviations**

  The Lorax, written by dr seuss, is a tale about the conservation of our natural resources.

Proofreading Sentences

Literature and Life 4

● **Capitalization, Quotation Marks**

Our teacher asked, who was the Goddess of flowers in Roman Mythology—Diana, Flora, or Helen?

● **Using the Right Word, Commas (To Set Off Long Phrases), Capitalization, Italics (Underlining Titles)**

In the novel The Prisoner of Zenda king Rudolf rules an country called ruritania.

● **Commas (To Set Off Long Phrases), Capitalization, Italics (Underlining Titles)**

Besides alice's adventures in wonderland Lewis Carroll wrote the hunting of the snark and a tangled tale.

● **Using the Right Word, Capitalization, Parallelism**

The hula hoop is named after that hawaiian dance in witch you sway your hips, keep your upper torso still, and then you move your arms and hands gently.

● **Capitalization, Rambling Sentence, Contractions**

Im glad I dont live in the stone age and, besides, I like the new fashions and all the modern conveniences and I'm also looking forward to driving a car.